Masala

Poems from India, Bangladesh, Pakistan and Sri Lanka

Masala

Poems from India, Bangladesh, Pakistan and Sri Lanka

Chosen by
Debjani Chatterjee

MACMILLAN CHILDREN'S BOOKS

For Nikhil, Nitesh, Pujya, Rohit, Rahul, Mithuna, Tejas,
Aditya Priyanath, Tanvi, Deesha, Shreya and Enakshi –
Munnu Mashi/Pishi

First published 2005
by Macmillan Children's Books
a division of Macmillan Publishers Limited
20 New Wharf Road, London N1 9RR
Basingstoke and Oxford
www.panmacmillan.com

Associated companies throughout the world

ISBN 0 330 41501 8

Printed by Mackays of Chatham plc, Kent.

Contents

FLAVOURS OF ASIA:
Poems About Food and Dress

THE NEW GAVASKAR: Poems About Work, School and Play

EAST IS EAST
People and Identity

from THE BALLAD OF EAST AND WEST

Oh, East is East, and West is West, and never the twain
   shall meet,
Till Earth and Sky stand presently at God's great
   Judgment Seat;
But there is neither East nor West, Border, nor Breed,
   nor Birth,
When two strong men stand face to face,
tho' they come from the ends of the earth!

Rudyard Kipling
(India and UK)

Rudyard Kipling (1865–1936) was born in Bombay (present-day Mumbai), India. His father worked at the Lahore Museum (now in Pakistan). His best books of fiction (*Plain Tales from the Hills*, *The Jungle Book* and *Kim*) and poetry (*Barrack-Room Ballads*) were inspired by India. His poem 'If' was voted 'the nation's most popular poem' in a BBC TV poll in 1995 and remains one of Britain's best-loved poems. The famous first line of 'The Ballad of East and West' is often quoted in support of the view that people from the East are too different from those of the West to allow a meeting point. But Kipling also stressed the common humanity of people in this poem.

PALANQUIN BEARERS

Lightly, O lightly we bear her along,
She sways like a flower in the wind of our song;
She skims like a bird on the foam of a stream,
She floats like a laugh from the lips of a dream.
Gaily, O gaily we glide and we sing,
We bear her along like a pearl on a string.

Softly, O softly we bear her along,
She hangs like a star in the dew of our song;
She springs like a beam on the brow of the tide,
She falls like a tear from the eyes of a bride.
Lightly, O lightly we glide and we sing,
We bear her along like a pearl on a string.

Sarojini Naidu
(India)

A palanquin is a covered litter carried by palanquin bearers. In India in the past, the wealthy, especially women, would travel in palanquins.

Sarojini Naidu (1879–1949) was a politician, educator and social reformer. She began writing poetry at a very young age and Mahatma Gandhi called her 'the Nightingale of India'. Her poetry books include: *The Golden Threshold*, *The Bird of Time* and *The Broken Wing*.

4

BENGAL

There once was a man of Bengal
Who was asked to a fancy dress ball;
    He murmured: 'I'll risk it
    and go as a biscuit . . .'
But a dog ate him up in the hall.

Anon.

Bengal was a large province under the British Raj (government) in India. But the British partitioned it in 1905 into East and West Bengal. In 1947, when India was partitioned, West Bengal remained in India while East Bengal became East Pakistan. In 1971, East Pakistan won independence and became Bangladesh.

SINDHI WOMAN

Barefoot through the bazaar,
and with the same undulant grace
as the cloth blown back from her face,
she glides with a stone jar
high on her head
and not a ripple in her tread.

Watching her cross erect
stones, garbage, excrement, and crumbs
of glass in the Karachi slums,
I, with my stoop, reflect
they stand most straight
who learn to walk beneath a weight.

Jon Stallworthy
(UK)

Bazaar: market. Along with many other words from Indian languages, 'bazaar' came into the English language during British rule in India.
Sindhi: someone from the Sind region who speaks the Sindhi language.
Undulant: swaying
Karachi: a busy port on the Arabian Sea, it is also Pakistan's business capital.

Jon Stallworthy, who wrote this poem, lived in Karachi, Pakistan, in the early 1960s.

AS AN ASIAN YOUNG WOMAN
I AM EXPECTED TO . . .

respect older people
        iron
speak Punjabi at home to my grandparents
        clean up
keep my body covered
not go out as much as boys
        behave
not to go out with boys
        clean
        cook
        respect
        study
get married (arranged)
clean, clean, clean

Asian Young Women at AWAAZ
Asian women's training centre
(Asian and UK)

Punjabi: the language spoken by someone from the Punjab region. The Punjab was partitioned and is today partly in India and partly in Pakistan.
This is a group poem by Asian Young Women at AWAAZ Asian women's training centre in Sheffield.

7

BRIDGE AND TEA PARTY

'My daughter,' says Mrs Shah,
'is S.S.C. pass, high Second Class,
Head girl in school, very interested
in life; we encourage it – pictures
parties shopping visiting
active child.'

'My Ayesha did her Cambridge abroad,
scholarship from British Council
she'll be settling in England or
the US on a green card.'

'My Renu is very popular
they call her Ren at college,
her name came in the papers
you know – students' revolt.'

'I'll call Bunty
darling sing what
teacher taught you
sing near aunty.'

Beheroze F. Shroff
(India and USA)

S.S.C.: an Indian school-leaving certificate.
Cambridge: a British school-leaving certificate.
Green card: document permitting a foreigner to settle in the USA.

TYPICAL MR PATEL'S
TYPICAL PROMOTION

Mr Patel, you're blah blah blah.
BUT . . .
Can you fill in this form – for equal opportunity?
It's to allow us to monitor you-know-what.
Thank you. We'll let you know in due course.
(Never.)

Mr Patel,
Sorry.

You were one of the two selected,
BUT . . .
(Hell, you smell of *masala*.)
Try again next year.
(And the year after, and after, and after . . .)
Thank you for your interest in our company.

The calf butted the oak:
Mr Patel bought the company
and promoted himself.

Yogesh Patel
(India, Kenya, Uganda and UK)

Masala: an Indian word for spices.

9

SONNEMUTU SPEAKING

Never heard of Darmapatti?
Middle of nowhere my village!
Edge of the jungle, India.

Our house – like the others,
mud walls gone hard as hard in the sun,
my Appa whitewashes every year. Nice.
Just the one room – mud floors too,
but Amma sweeps and polishes, so smooth and shiny.

The roof's all plaited leaves and grasses –
dry as anything inside.
Beds? Chairs? You're joking!
Mats are fine, and Appa's fixed a rope
to hang our stuff over.

Played with other kids
until they went to school.
Begged and begged to go –
they shook their heads though and look sad.
Whatever was the matter?

Went on a bus one day with Amma and Appa,
night when we arrived. So many people,
shops all lit up, lorries, carts, cars I saw . . . scary!

In this sort of house, children everywhere.
One kind lady sat and gave me funny things to do.
Amma and Appa smiled, they hugged and hugged
and then they went away.

My chest went up and down, my face
all wet for days, nights too.
Then it dried up; I joined the kids,
pulled funny faces with our mouths,
made tongues wag up and down,
felt noises in our throats, did sums and letters.

I found I was at school! A very special school
for kids like me – turned out that we were 'deaf'.
I jumped for joy.
Just 'deaf' – that's all that was the matter!

Ruth Dalton
(UK)

Darmapatti: a village in South India.
Amma and Appa: Mother and Father.

CONVERSATION BETWEEN AUNT AND NIECE

(For Piyali)

Aunt, aunt, what's that in your hair?
A broken comb, I've just shampooed my hair.

Aunt, aunt, what are those marks under your eyes?
The ink of time, soap doesn't wash it off.

Aunt, aunt, what are those things in your sky?
The crooked arguments of bare branches.

Aunt, aunt, what's that creeper against your garage?
The northern jasmine, flowers in August.

Aunt, aunt, what are those things flying in the distance,
                    in between the trees?
Bed-sheets, pillow-cases, your uncle's shirts. Washed
by my hands.

Aunt, aunt, all around us there are so many dead leaves,
                half-dead weeds, elderly mosses,
yet why does it all look so lovely?

Because suddenly today, in mid-December,
at eleven in the morning, pushing aside his quilt of mist,
the sun's decided to get up.

Ketaki Kushari Dyson
(India and England) Translated by the poet

'MY TALENTED COUSIN'

Out each morning
delivering
papers.

Afternoon spent
behind a shop
counter.

Evenings
Indian restaurant –
very exclusive,
waitering.

He's got
two degrees
business and philosophy.

Hamid Shami
(Pakistan and UK)

GIFTS OF THE PAST WEEK

My maternal grandma sent us dried fish on Monday.
My paternal grandma sent us mangoes on Tuesday.
My maternal aunt sent us *shatkora* on Wednesday.
My paternal aunt sent us *koi* fish on Thursday.
My maternal uncle sent us a chatty letter on Friday.
My paternal uncle sent us *kadamba* flowers on Saturday.
My sister-in-law sent us henna on Sunday.
On Monday my mother and I were as happy as
    could be!

Mehrun Nessa (aged 14)
(Bangladesh and UK)
Translated by Safuran Ara and Debjani Chatterjee

Shatkora: a yellowish vegetable with a lemon fragrance.
Koi fish: a tasty delicacy.
Kadamba flowers: round yellow-white flowers that grow in the
Monsoon season.
Henna: a reddish dye (called mehndi in South Asia) obtained
from the leaves of the henna plant. It is used as a hair-dye and
to decorate parts of the body, especially the hands and the feet.
Flowers, leaves, stars and other motifs are used in decoration. It
is customary for some communities to decorate their brides
with henna.

14

SPECIAL GIFTS

Can I send you some special gifts, for your
birthday, dear brother?
Paper boats that rocked in the monsoon
puddles of yesteryears and sand temples
built on the shores of time . . .
A pack of those weird giggles that you lost –
I snatched them off my pupils the other day;
Some silly songs sung from atop the walls
you once scaled – they were rising out of a
twinkle in my eye;
A few deafening Bruce Lee screams that still
pierce my ears and all the names you've called
me – I've saved them in my smiles;
And then, those *Vellichapad* days – when dowsed
in saffron and turmeric, you danced in glee to
Amma's angry shouts . . .

Usha Kishore
(India and UK)

Vellichapad: Malayalam (a language spoken in Kerala, South
India) word for oracle. Many temples in Kerala have their
oracles. During temple festivals the oracles dance in ecstasy.

AN ALIEN, I . . .

I use your disguises:
close my mouth and ears
on every train and bus.

Occasionally, I break out,
wear gold and silk and khaddar,

when you don't look at me
a little more energetically than usual

and the seat next to me
is always the last to be occupied.

Prabhu S. Guptara
(India and UK)

Khaddar: handmade cloth, made from cotton usually spun at home.

GRANDPA'S NOSE

GOR-GOR, GER-GER
How tuneful is the thunder!

No, it's not the thundercloud
but Grandpa's nose that sounds so loud!

Sunirmal Bosu
(India)
Translated by Debjani Chatterjee

Sunirmal Bosu was an Indian poet well known for his writing for children. His birth centenary was celebrated in 2004.

GRANDMOTHER

Rain falls on warm tin roofs
like a thousand pearls.

The air is thick with ripe mangoes,
chickens scratch in the yard,

Bibi stands on the veranda
holding me in a tight hug,
her perfume of betel nut.

On the night she died
I dreamt of her:
of carrying water
to quench her thirst.

Contributor to First Words
(Bangladeshi and UK)

Bibi: the grandmother in this poem. Bibi is also a common name
for a woman.
Veranda: a balcony or gallery along the outside of a building.
The word has come into English from Portuguese via Hindi.
Betel nut: the seed of the fruit of the betel palm, chewed by
many South Asians.

WHEN JASWINDER LETS LOOSE HER HAIR

When Jaswinder lets loose her hair
it flows like a stream
that could run around a mosque.

Below her knees it thins
to a wild sparseness
as if the wind tugged at it

when as a girl she sped
across the formal garden.
I crave Jaswinder's hair,

coiled – dark and smooth
as a glazed pot, falling –
a torrent of midnight rain.

Moniza Alvi
(Pakistan and UK)

19

BEDEH

This is the name of my clan.
I am a water-gypsy
on the turbulent rivers of Bangladesh.
My boat is home
to me, my wife, and our children.

I have some knowledge of words
and wild herbs.
I treat snake-bites,
drive out evil spirits,
and attempt things which others dare not.
Tigers, robbers, snakes, demons, storms
all seem to leave me alone!

My needs are small and simple.
They are easily met
from day to day,
from hand to mouth,
from one river-bend settlement
to the next.

Sometimes in fine weather
I row out to the river's end.
I meet many ships at the anchorage.
The crew exchanges foodstuffs,
old clothes, newspapers,
empty cans and bottles
with my beads, bangles,
bamboo-toys and seashells.

Once I had a chance to board
an English ship.
I marvelled at the ocean-going craft.
But the Captain, he marvelled: at me,
at the size of my boat,
at how we had survived, and at how we live!
He wrote down our names,
and other things in his notebook.
He said, one day he would write about us.

I cannot imagine
why would anyone want
to do that!

Shafi Ahmed
(Bangladesh and UK)

Bedeh: a tribe of water-gypsies who live on boats in Bangladesh.
Anchorage: a place for anchoring or tying a boat.
Shafi Ahmed (b. 1937) was born in Bangladesh and travelled the
world as an engineer in the Merchant Navy. 'Bedeh' won a
Peterloo Poets Prize in 1992.

THE STREET HEALER
OF KARACHI

On a not-too-quiet, not-too-busy street
In the shade of a great Jamun tree
Against a paint-peeling wall
On a rickety wooden platform
Held by three legs and a rock,
Sits an ancient man, peering at passers-by
Through thick spectacle lenses.
A poster roped to the wall behind
States his age-old profession.
Scattered on his platform
Are bottles, tubes, and jars:
Of yellow pills, white pills,
Red water, pink powder,
All made by gnarled hands
With the pain of life and age.
He is not a medical practitioner.
He sells a few ancient remedies
To feed many hungry mouths.

Shehnaz Somjee
(Pakistan and UK)

Jamun: a kind of black plum that grows in South Asian countries. It is also called a rose-apple.

LITTLE OLD MAN

Little old man, you spread a Himalayan shadow.

Your smiling nut-brown face, your skimpy loin-cloth,
your sandals, round glasses, spinning wheel, your
    peasant
diet, mere necessities, threadbare ideas,
made you a laughing stock. What a shocker you were!
But your far-seeing vision persisted until
your mockers were uncomfortable in their scorn.

Splindly legs bestrode continents
though Britannia ruled the waves.

I salute you, hero of the third-class carriages.

When you clutched a fistful of salt
on the sands of the Dandi beach,

the world saw that the sands of history ran out
for colonialism and all such tyrannies.
You marched, you fasted, you kept silence and trusted
in *Satyagraha* to demonstrate that *Swaraj*
is self-help, self-made, and your wooden walking stick

could break the Raj's mighty back.
Terrier-like, you kept your grip
on the scruff of the bulldog's neck.

I honour you as one who rejected honours.
Mahatma, you led your nation to its future.
Your torch was the flare that lit a conflagration
of truth to burn away the vice of oppression.

The assassin's bullet splashed its shameful stain of red,
it stopped your words of prayer, but your life had said
    it all.
I salute you, hero of the third-class carriages.
Little Old Man, your immortal shadow spreads and
    spreads.

Debjani Chatterjee
(India and UK)

Himalayan: the Himalayas or Himalayan mountains, north of
India and Pakistan, are the greatest mountain range in the world.
Spinning wheel: during India's freedom movement Gandhi
called on Indians to boycott British-manufactured cloth and to
use the spinning wheel to make their own cloth.
Dandi: Mumbai sea-beach where Gandhi led a huge crowd of
Indians to symbolically break the law on manufacturing salt.
Satyagraha: truth-force.
Swaraj: self-rule.
Raj: Indian word for 'government'. British rule in India is called
the British Raj.
Mahatma: title popularly given to the politician-saint Mohandas
Karamchand Gandhi (1889–1948), it means 'Great Soul'.
Gandhi, who was also called 'Father of the nation', was famous
for his simple life-style.
Conflagration: a big fire.

FAITH

There are things
you need not know
my mother once said
when I pricked my balloon
to discover what hid inside.

There are things
you need not know
my father once said
when I pricked my finger
to see how I bled.

There are things
you will fail to find
both my parents said
when I flew from their nest
to explore my brave new world.

Shanta Acharya
(India and UK)

THE LAST MOUNTAIN

Story Poems

AN EPIC ABRIDGED

In *Ramayana*
          brave Rama Chandra,
                    Prince of Ayodhya,
                              was wed to Sita.
                    Sita loved Rama,
          Rama loved Sita.
Demon Ravana,
          tyrant of Lanka,
                    kidnapped sweet Sita.
                              Monkeys helped Rama
                    build from India
          a bridge to Lanka,
They caused much brouha,
          besieging Lanka,
                    killing Ravana.
                              Rama and Sita
                    flew to Ayodhya
          to shouts of 'Hurrah!
Light every *diya*
          for Rama Chandra
                    will be our Raja.
                              Diwali hurrah!
                    Rama and Sita,
          back in Ayodhya!

Light every *diya*,
　　throughout Ayodhya!
　　　　Shout Hurrah! Hurrah!
　　　　　Jai Sita Rama!
　　　　Hail Rama Sita!
　　　Jai Rama Sita!
　　Hail Sita Rama!'

Debjani Chatterjee
(India and UK)

Epic: a long poem that tells a heroic story

Ramayana: ancient Indian epic in Sanskrit by Valmiki, it tells the story of Rama and Sita. It has been retold many times in many languages and continues to inspire all the art forms of many Asian countries.

Ravana: ten-headed demon king.

Diya: little oil and cotton wick lamps. These are especially lit at Diwali, the festival of light, to celebrate the return to Ayodhya (a city in North India) of Rama and Sita and the triumph of good over evil.

Raja: an Indian word for 'king'.

Jai Sita Rama, etc.: a mantra or chant, it means, 'Victory to Sita and Rama'.

THREE BLIND MEN
DESCRIBE AN ELEPHANT

It's very hard and smooth and long like time.
It curves towards the sky; its point is fierce.

It must be like a bird with leather wings.
When I touch this it flaps ready for flight.

No, no, this is a tree, well-rooted, strong.
Its bark is hairy, rough like man's justice.

Simon Fletcher
(UK)

LAKSHMANA'S REGRET

She could have taught humility
itself the meaning of 'humble';
but I was too proud to accept
her simple devotion – I was not my brother.

She was like the wild Jujube tree
growing outside her hut –
scraggly, small and thin,
with grey bark cracked,
but O she was evergreen!

Praise the Mother, that one of us brothers
could be a loving son,
for I saw only a wrinkled hag
who delayed us with opportuning.

I marked Elder Brother's reverence
and bowed in silent reverie.
I never had his ease with women,
young or old. Demoness, goddess,
princess or beggar – I armoured myself
against their sorcery. I was not my brother.

He sat down to bask in her love,
for all the world as if Sita did not weep
and Ravana did not wait for his nemesis.

My baffling brother stretched a greedy palm
in which old Shabari placed her berries
like so many sugar-plums – all her worldly wealth,
each fruit bitten and sweetness-tested
for offering to her princely guests.

Elder Brother relished those berries
but my finicky delicacy
made me throw away my share
with a careless discretion.
I was not my brother.

Later he said that Shabari was a celestial –
and Elder Brother never lied.
I forgot the incident until

many moons later when I died.

My head on Brother's lap, the juice
of divine Sanjivani was squeezed into my mouth,
and I revived to be told
that the life-giving herb had grown
from those berries carelessly sown.

Debjani Chatterjee
(India and UK)

Lakshmana: Rama's loyal younger brother in the *Ramayana*. On
the way to rescue Sita from the demon Ravana, they encounter
Shabari. Rama's blessing releases Shabari from a curse so that
she can return to Heaven. The epic tells this story, as well as the
one in which the Sanjivani herb restores Lakshmana to life.

THE SNAKE-CHARMER'S WIFE

'Oh why is he late? – Oh why is he late?'
The snake-charmer's wife said again and again.
'Perhaps he is drunk – how long shall I wait? –
Not knowing the truth just adds to my pain.'

At the sun's dropping down she went out and ran
to the old women who carried their pails to the well:
'Oh please tell me true – have you seen my fine man? –
My snake-charmer husband – Oh tell me – Oh tell.

You cannot mistake him – he's hairy and fat,
his belly is large – with long drinkings of wine,
he's always in mischief – just like an old cat,
but despite it I love him – because he is mine.'

'We did notice something stretched out in the lane,
perhaps it's a monkey – perhaps it's a man,
perhaps he is drunk – perhaps he's in pain.
You better go quickly and do what you can.'

She found him laid there with a wound in his arm.
Despite the dim light it looked savage and red,
that snake had not swayed to the power of his charm,
and now he was poisoned – perhaps he was dead.

She knelt on the ground and sucked at the bite,
then covered it over with herbs that would heal,
she said prayers to Rama throughout the long night
that he would behold her and hear her appeal.

And then in the dawning his eyes opened wide,
his toes and his fingers all started to move.
She felt so relieved that she cried and she cried –
for despite all his failings he was her great love.

He moved all his limbs until they were free
and then to her joy he suddenly pranced.
Before she could guess it, he grasped her with glee,
and there in the dawning they danced and they danced.

Ian Emberson
(UK)

33

A FISTFUL OF MUD

A fistful of mud enters Gopal's mouth of mischief,
   but Mother Yashoda stops him from swallowing.
She peeks into a toothless grin where all cosmic space
   with suns and moons and planets is revolving.

Debjani Chatterjee
(India and UK)

Gopal: Krishna is a popular Hindu god who was called Gopal
as a baby.
Yashoda: Krishna's foster mother.

THE LAST MOUNTAIN

Once we mountains sported wings,
soared proud above the heavens,
frolicked among fleecy clouds
and slid up and down the rainbows
that groaned with our mighty weight.
Rushing wind was our element;
we played the music of the spheres.
The sky gifted us a giddy lightness
that stole the breath away.

But we took our freedom for granted
and jealous gods have clipped our wings.
Now distant thunder growls our grumbles
as my brothers and sisters tower in dreams
of how we once were monarchs of the air.
Yet I, the smallest of the mountains,
escaped the wrath of gods.
I hide in the frothing ocean and, sleepless,
I bide my time with folded wings.
The sea soil rumbles my secret songs
as I call to my family to take heart.
Their trust will strengthen me
and lift me up to strike a blow for our kind,
to fly up to the sun itself if need be,
to dance in our remembered freedom,
for faith, they say, moves mountains.

Debjani Chatterjee (UK)

Mountains once had wings, according to Indian myths. When
the gods cut their wings, one mountain hid in the ocean and
causes tidal waves when it flaps its wings.

OOPS! DON'T LOSE
YOUR HEAD!

He didn't do what Shiva said,
so little Ganesh lost his head.
Parvati, she was really mad
and said; 'You're such an awful dad!'

'Just look what you've done to our son,
thank goodness he's the only one!
Now you had better put things right
unless you want a stand-up fight.'

Shiva said; 'Oops! Don't lose your cool
I know I've been a holy fool.
I came to visit but instead
I'll go and get our son a head.'

Poor Shiva left and tried his best
but did he pass or fail the test?
Do you find Ganesh triumphant
with the head of an elephant?

Brian D'Arcy
(UK)

Shiva: third god of the Hindu trinity of Creator, Saviour and
Destroyer.
Ganesh: elephant-headed god of Wisdom and Parvati's elder son.
Parvati: Shiva's wife and daughter of the Himalayas.

LEAVING
THE VILLAGE

Travel and Landscape

PEOPLE ASK

My father travelled from Ceylon
Island of cinnamon and rubies
To my mother's birthplace
In the heart of Yorkshire

People ask
Where do you come from?
I say:
From more places
than you imagine
My father's memories
My mother's dreams
Mines of gems and coal
Mango sunsets over rhubarb fields

People ask
Which half of you is white?
I say:
There are no halves in me
Everything is whole
I am a myriad of mingling
Multicoloured stories
Whispering wisely down
through centuries

People ask
Where do you belong?
I say:
In the world
In my father's hopes
In my mother's songs
Most of all
In the place inside myself
Shining with its own futures

Seni Seneviratne
(Sri Lanka and UK)

Ceylon: a country now known as Sri Lanka.
Cinnamon: a spice. Also a tree in Sri Lanka whose bark is used
as a spice.

THE FURTHER BANK

I long to go over there to the further bank of the river,
Where those boats are tied to the bamboo poles in a line;
Where men cross over in their boats in the morning
    with ploughs on their shoulders to till their
    faraway fields;
Where the cowherds make their lowing cattle swim
    across to the riverside pasture;
Whence they all come back home in the evening,
    leaving the jackals to howl in the island overgrown
    with weeds.
Mother, if you don't mind, I should like to become the
    boatman of the ferry when I am grown up.

They say there are strange pools hidden behind that
    high bank,
Where flocks of wild ducks come when the rains are
    over, and thick reeds grow round the margins
    where waterbirds lay their eggs;
Where snipes with their dancing tails stamp their tiny
    footprints upon the clean soft mud;
Where in the evening the tall grasses crested with white
    flowers invite the moonbeam to float upon their
    waves.
Mother, if you don't mind, I should like to become the
    boatman of the ferry when I am grown up.

I shall cross and cross back from bank to bank, and all
    the boys and girls of the village will wonder at me
    while they are bathing.

When the sun climbs the mid sky and morning wears
    on to noon, I shall come running to you, saying,
    'Mother, I am hungry!'
When the day is done and the shadows cower under
    he trees, I shall come back in the dusk.
I shall never go away from you into the town to work
    like father.
Mother, if you don't mind, I should like to become the
    boatman of the ferry when I am grown up.

Rabindranath Tagore
(India)

Rabindranath Tagore (1861–1941), the national poet of India,
wrote the national anthems of India and Bangladesh. He also
wrote novels, short stories, essays and plays, composed songs,
painted, acted and was an educator. He won the Nobel Prize for
Literature in 1913.

I AM A DAUGHTER OF
A RIVERINE LAND

I am an ordinary girl of Bangladesh,
I am a daughter of a riverine land.
I know that so many different types
of rivers dance throughout Bengal –
Padma, Meghna, Jamuna, Ichhamati.
I am their daughter, and of the rivers
Dhaleshwari and Aatrai.
The rivers of my land are my mothers;
their maternal love has blessed me.

The rivers of my land have so many forms!
This land of six seasons
is our own Bangladesh.
All six seasons have at various times
moulded our rivers.

In the monsoon season the rivers
take on a fearsome appearance.
Floods wash away both banks
and riverside dwellers lose their way.
But the alluvial soil left by the flood
blesses the land with a golden harvest.
The farmer's wife is jubilant
and the farmer forgets all
the distress of the season of floods.

Sitting by the riverside, the farmer's wife
talks of so many things to the river.
She confides what is in her heart.
She calls to the boatmen
whose vessels sail past:
'O Boatman Brother, tell my father
to fetch me home.'

After rain, the river is most beautiful.
Sitting on the river bank
in the moonlit night,
the shepherds, on their flutes, play
the music of union and separation.

This Bangladesh of ours
is a land of rivers and soil,
a poet's land,
a land for singing, a land for living.
No matter how often I relate
the stories of this land
and of its rivers,
they never end.
To write it all
would result
in a great epic
whose end cannot be written.

Gulshan Ara (Bangladesh)
Translated by Debjani Chatterjee

Padma, Meghna, Jamuna, Ichhamati, Dhaleshwari and Aatrai:
rivers in Bangladesh.

MAP OF INDIA

If I stare at the country long enough
I can prise it off the paper,
lift it like a flap of skin.

Sometimes it's an Advent calendar –
each city has a window
which I leave open
a little wider each time.

India is manageable – smaller than
my hand, the Mahanadi River
thinner than my lifeline.

Moniza Alvi
(Pakistan and UK)

Advent: a period including four Sundays before Christmas.
Mahanadi: an Indian river, its name means 'Great River'.

Moniza Alvi (b. 1954) has a mixed Pakistani and English heritage.

AMONG THE FLOWERS

What is it, shadow-like, among the flowers?
The breeze plays hide-and-seek among the flowers.

The perfume was so heady that my head throbbed;
I could not bear to sit among the flowers.

The moon also appeared between the branches:
a new bloom unfolded among the flowers.

My moon is distinct, set apart from the stars,
my blossom is unique among the flowers.

The light from the moon radiated fragrance,
while sunshine colours danced among the flowers.

Butterflies and turtle-doves all flew away,
while I stayed deep in sleep among the flowers.

What causes your hand to hesitate, Basir?
Could there have been a thorn among the flowers?

Basir Sultan Kazmi
(Pakistan and UK)
Translated by the author and Debjani Chatterjee

This poem is written as an Urdu ghazal, a form of lyrical poetry
and song that is extremely popular in India and Pakistan.

Basir Sultan Kazmi (b. 1955) was born in Lahore.

COROMANDEL FISHERS

Rise, brothers, rise, the wakening skies pray
    to the morning light,
The wind lies asleep in the arms of the dawn
    like a child that has cried all night.
Come, let us gather our nets from the shore,
    and set our catamarans free,
To capture the leaping wealth of the tide, for
    we are the sons of the sea.

No longer delay, let us hasten away in the
    track of the seagull's call,
The sea is our mother, the cloud is our brother,
    the waves are our comrades all.
What though we toss at the fall of the sun
    where the hand of the sea-god drives?
He who holds the storm by the hair, will hide
    in his breast our lives.

Sweet is the shade of the coconut glade, and
    the scent of the mango grove,
And sweet are the sands at the full o' the
    moon with the sound of the voices we love.
But sweeter, O brothers, the kiss of the spray
    and the dance of the wild foam's glee:
Row, brothers, row to the blue of the verge,
    where the low sky mates with the sea.

Sarojini Naidu (India)

Coromandel: Kerala in South India was called Coromandel
under British rule.
Catamaran: a swift-sailing boat with two hulls side by side.

LEAVING THE VILLAGE

Rickshaws dance in the street
the bus horn moans long and low
we squash up on the plastic seat
sacks, chickens, people close.
A cow calls for its calf
in the village, across the terai
and footprints are lost in the dark
as the milky moon skims the sky.
We awake as the traffic slows
and our bus politely rolls aside
hundreds of chillies are in the road
like painted nails, in the sun to dry.
Chillies! like blood, like lips curled
leaving their soil for England
as footsteps are taken all over the world
and memories burn my tongue.

Selina Rodrigues
(Anglo-Indian and UK)

Rickshaw: a small two-wheeled carriage pulled or pedalled by a man.
Terai: a belt of marshy jungle between the plains of North India and the Himalayas.

HUNGRY GHOST

Today I went shopping with my father
after many years. I felt I was back
in time to when I'd follow grandfather
to the market, smelling the spicy scents,
drinking the sights and mingling with the shouts.
Neither buyer nor seller, I would float
like a restless spirit, hungry for life.

The market is bigger. I have grown too.
There are more goods as distances have shrunk.
The prices are higher. I understand
about money and, alas, its bondage
of buyers and sellers. Almost I wish
I was again that hungry ghost, watchful
and floating through the world's noisy bazaar.

Debjani Chatterjee
(India and UK)

IN THE DESERT

When grandma took me to Quetta
the train cut through sugar cane
and maize fields across the Punjab
and entered the Thar desert.

I stood at the window for hours
and watched the sand of the desert
meet the sandy beach of the sky
where the heat-haze broke in waves.

It was the first time that I'd seen
a world in which there seemed
nothing to live for and nothing
with which to keep one alive.

I had a fantasy as children do
of being alone in the desert
and lasting there for no longer
than a drop of water.

I stood at the window for hours
and wanted to know for how long
the world as far as I could see
would continue completely empty.

Now thirty years later when I look back
on that journey through the desert
I feel I am still at the window
searching the horizon for plants.

Zulfikar Ghose
(Pakistan and USA)

Quetta: capital of the mountainous Baluchistan province in Pakistan.
Punjab: a region in north-west India and Pakistan, its name means 'land of five rivers'.
Thar: a desert in northern India and Pakistan.

A HARVEST OF WHEAT

All day the sounds of scythes
Cutting stalks. Our hands sticky
With juices, our arms heavy
With swathes of wheat.

All day in the blazing sun.
Our backs arched, eyes focused
On the sharp blade and the stems.
Slicing and gathering systematically.

All day in a kind of communion:
My father reciting the Koran;
My brothers and cousins and nephews
Exchanging stories and jokes. Our lives

Intermingling, growing around words.
Above us, the crows caw all day.
By evening there are bales of wheat
Scattered in an open field.

The women near the edges make
Nan bread. The scent of dough,
Baking, comforts our exhausted bodies.
Embers float up into the navy sky.

One by one stars begin to glimmer.
We navigate ourselves towards Mecca.
My father's voice rises between us.
His words crumble in my mouth.

Tariq Latif
(Pakistan and UK)

Nan: a kind of soft Indian bread.
Mecca: a city in Saudi Arabia that is the holiest city for Muslims.
'Navigating' towards Mecca means facing Mecca for the ritual
Islamic prayers.

BOAT RIDE

The boat
hollowed tree
with bamboo hoods,
a floating house.
Under one hood
boiled the cooking pot;
the other covered our bed.

So we glided up-river.
Kaka was the man
with the gun.
We passed paddy fields,
banks of watermelons,
then came to a copse
where trees wore flocks
of green pigeons.
Silence, silence, children.
With finger on lip
Kaka leapt
from the boat.
The boys followed,
but I was told
to stay.

Water echoed
the thud of shots.
I rushed to see the spoil,
disobeying Father.

Birds, green birds,
with still wings
strung on a pole,
no more flashing
the green of the jungle.

My feet slipped,
I slithered neck-deep
into the river,
and was dragged
a rag-doll
most misshapen,
and gently reprimanded
by Father.
I shook
with fear of near-death,
I spread my wet hair
like feathers.

Amiti Grech
(Bangladesh and UK)

Kaka: an Indian term for 'Uncle'.

MONSOON

Born into it, one learns
to understand this rain.
It falls and falls, not
in squalls and squirts,
but a solid sheet of
stainless steel that hits
the ground, edgewise;
or aided by the wind
with hard fingers it combs
the grass. When it slackens,
as now, each strand is
an auger that drills the
earth to its dark centre.

To the others, a topic,
of how or what it renews
through the weeks, a wonder
at the sureness of its coming,
or an inconvenience
upsetting flight schedules.
But to us it is a
personage, as venerable
as great-grandfather, still
full of pep, who skips
up the steps, and halts
half-way along the veranda,
dripping, redolent of
mango-pulp, paddy and mud.

Taufiq Rafat
(Pakistan)

Monsoon: a season of rain in South Asia.
Squalls: sudden burst of wind, often accompanied by rain.
Augur: a prophet or soothsayer.
Venerable: worthy of reverence.
Pep: vigour.
Redolent: having a pleasant smell.

Taufiq Rafat (1927–98) was one of Pakistan's best poets to write in English.

STRENGTH

You send strong winds to blow me down,
But I am straight and tall;
I am like the willow.
I bend but never fall.

Your storms may cause a branch to break,
My body aches for sleep;
But wasted is your vicious scorn,
I cry but never weep.

You tempt me with life's luscious fruits
And try to lead me from my way;
But I reject your poisoned smiles,
I err, but never stray.

Kailash Puri
(India and UK)

LOST

To quote my distant friend Imran MacLeod
'A man with culture has no identity'.

The last I heard from him was, he was off
To the Himalayas.

He had a very confused childhood.

Father was Scottish.
Mother Pakistani.

They'd always be arguing over many things
Concerning him.

One was religion.

Father wanted him brought up
A Catholic; mother wanted a Muslim.

Was the only boy on our street who went
To mosque on Fridays and chapel on Sundays.

But in the mountains

God's sure to find him.

Hamid Shami
(Pakistan and UK)

ABROAD

Anything goes when abroad.

All who come to these foreign parts –
all seem to change somehow
in dress and in attire,
in speech and in behaviour.
Even though food habits change,
one wants to hold on to the substance.
Yet, all seem to change somehow.

They came, saying that from this point
onwards life would begin anew.
Dear ones, home and possessions,
all were left behind;
so much to call one back,
so many memories that divert.
Yet, all seem to change somehow.

Anything goes when abroad.
Being seen to be phoney seems to hurt us all.
Yet, all seem to change somehow.

Safuran Ara
(Bangladesh and UK)
Translated from the Bengali by Debjani Chatterjee

TANKA

A letter from home
wafts in the smell of sand
in the monsoon rains –
dusk falls and I hear the peal
of temple bells in the wind . . .

Usha Kishore
(India and UK)

Tanka: a five-line poem which first originated in Japan 1200
years ago.

THE MANGO TREE

Tree, most certain,
right at the boulevard's end
just before the fountain,
mango tree,
I cannot pass that way
without paying homage
to your shape.
It is midwinter.
On either side, the traffic
flows past, but you stand
compact in the morning wind
under skies now blue now grey
with a green integrity.

Taufiq Rafat
(Pakistan)

THE PICNIC IN JAMMU

Uncle Ayub swung me round and round
till the horizon became a rail
banked high upon the Himalayas.
The trees signalled me past. I whistled,
shut my eyes through tunnels of the air.
The family laughed, watching me puff
out my muscles, healthily aggressive.

This was late summer, before the snows
come to Kashmir, this was picnic time.

Then, uncoupling me from the sky, he
plunged me into the river, himself
a bough with me dangling at its end.
I went purple as a plum. He reared
back and lowered the branch of his arm
to grandma who swallowed me with a kiss.
Laughter peeled away my goose pimples.

This was late summer, before the snows
come to Kashmir, this was picnic time.

After we'd eaten, he aimed grapes at
my mouth. I flung at him the shells of
pomegranates and ran off. He tracked
me down the river-bank. We battled,
melon-rind and apple-core our arms.
'You two!' grandma cried. 'Stop fighting, you'll
tire yourselves to death!' We didn't listen.

This was late summer, before the snows
come to Kashmir, this was picnic time.

Zulfikar Ghose
(Pakistan and USA)

Kashmir: a region that is partly in North India and partly in
Pakistan.

PALM-TREE

Palm-tree: single-legged giant,
    topping the other trees,
      peering at the firmament –
It longs   to pierce the black cloud-ceiling
    and fly away, away,
      if only it had wings.

The tree   seems to express its wish
    in the tossing of its head:
      its fronds heave and swish –
It thinks,   Maybe my leaves are feathers,
    and nothing stops me now
      from rising on their flutter.

All day   the fronds on the windblown tree
    soar and flap and shudder
      as though it thinks it can fly,
as though   it wanders in the skies,
    travelling who knows where,
      wheeling past the stars –

And then   as soon as the wind dies down,
    the fronds subside, subside:
      the mind of the tree returns
To earth,   recalls that earth is its mother:
    and then it likes once more
      its earthly corner.

Rabindranath Tagore
(India)

TROPICAL SUNSET

The sun goes down
   A luckless balloon
      Leaving a spray of gold in the air

Quick, children, run
   Through the ruins of the sun
      Catch the gold in your hair

For soon it will fade
   And the sky will shrink
      And frame the window of night

Kaiser Haq
(Bangladesh)

THE LASCAR'S SONG

We were sailing for Liverpool –
The Arabian Sea was rough
But Aden was very novel
Peddlers sold leathery stuff
Soon the boat was furrowing Suez
The boat cast anchor where Sudan was
From now on the air became cool –
We were sailing for Liverpool.

We were sailing. The engine-room smell
Was familiar to a lascar.
Leaving Bombay you pined
For your home, voyaging far –
The lights of Lisbon you could see
And in the distance – Stromboli.
A lascar was used to the sea's green,
We were sailing – into the unseen.

Rajat Kumar Biswas
(India and UK)

Lascar: a term once commonly used for a South Asian seaman.
Aden: main port of modern-day Yemen.
Suez: Egyptian port at the entrance to the Suez Canal, a man-made shipping canal connecting the Mediterranean Sea with the Red Sea.
Stromboli: a volcanic island in the north of Sicily.

Rajat Kumar Biswas (1923–2003) was born in India and lived in Britain for most of his life. 'The Lascar's Song' is the title poem of one of his collections.

LOCOMOTION

In brilliant sunshine, the Kolkata train
Goes swaying and clattering over the plain
While children look up, with incredulous eye
To see '*Babu* Loco' go thundering by.

Could tiger be fleeter or elephant stronger?
The train to Kolkata grows longer and longer;
Through pasture and paddy field, village and farm,
The shriek of his whistle still signals alarm.

In driving monsoon up the sheer mountainside,
In pained resignation, the passengers ride;
While engines are straining, laborious and slow,
With the sky high above, the ravine far below.

For millions of miles and through decades unnumbered,
These vintage 'rail-*garis*' have trundled and lumbered.
Through riot and rebellion, when hope seems in vain,
There's nothing so sure as the Indian train.

Win Saha
(UK)

Babu: a Bengali and Hindi term for 'Mister'.
Ravine: a deep narrow cleft or gorge.
Vintage: old and with an enduring classic appeal.
Garis: a Bengali and Hindi term for cars.

MIGRANTS

We migrated before we moved,
the gestures that we knew
were sown into new garments;
new words emerged
from our lips.
We learned to drink
tea from cups
and water in glasses.
Knives and forks
replaced our fingers,
but the cuisine was stubborn
demanding its own etiquette.
Our shoes were laced,
neatly tied up
we were delivered
into the service of a new age
despairing of our inheritance.

We read comics, chewed gum
drank Coke from bottles,
watched John Wayne shoot Indians
as we clapped.
Then Marilyn Monroe smiled.
Aftershave arrived
Hollywood style.
The radio blasted us with rock and roll
and we learned to dance
for a dollar or a dime
and signed our future on dotted lines.

We migrated before we moved;
the other place came to us.

Mahmood Jamal
(India, Pakistan and UK)

Etiquette: rules of manners.
John Wayne: a Hollywood movie star of many Westerns.
Marilyn Monroe: a seductive Hollywood movie star.

A BUS RIDE IN BIRMINGHAM

On the bus into town
the old woman gets up,
steadies herself with her stick
and almost past the stop
calls out *'Ruko, ruko!'*
waving her stick,

and as he slows the bus
and stops
and she is getting off
the driver says
'You should 'a pressed de bell, love',

and on we go
to slow again
to where the people will get on
who will get off at Chinatown,
and when they get on a woman
looks up from reading Graham Greene
and smiles *Hello*,

and afterwards, at home,
I write the poem
of this one journey in many
across the Brum world.

David Hart (UK)

Ruko, ruko: Hindi for Stop! Stop!
Graham Greene: a well-known novelist and winner of the Nobel
Prize for Literature.
Brum: slang for Birmingham.

MON-DORIA

Mon-doria,
    my heart's river,
        overflowing
            with joy and song,
        you skip softly,
    sweetly, through light
and shadow in
    the Sunderban.
        Your salaams touch
            towns and hamlets
        on your endless
    travels. You call
us, ceaselessly
    murmuring. Moss
        and a thousand
            weeds turn the swift
        whirlpool of dreams,
desires and hopes.
Your waters flow
    in faith, blowing
        like a sari
            in the wind, strong
        and calm to reach
    your noble end:

to make deserts
      bloom – paradise
            here on earth now.
                  Mon-doria,
            my heart's river,
      overflowing
with joy and song.

Rashida Islam
(Bangladesh)

Sundarban: the name means 'beautiful forest', it is a forested
region of Bangladesh.
Salaams: salutations.

SNAKES ALIVE!

Animal Poems

TIGER

A colour splasher
A stripe flasher
An eye gleamer
A wide beamer
A sleek sprinter
A smart hunter
A lone prowler
A loud growler
A night walker
A deer stalker
A soft sneaker
A strong striker
A swift pouncer
A quick bouncer
A fierce snarler
A cruel mauler
A great fighter
A bad biter
A meat eater
A man hater

Usha Kishore
(India and UK)

The Royal Bengal Tiger is the national animal of Bangladesh and India.

HAIKU

children panicking
out of the tiger cage
a wasp

David Cobb
(UK)

THE FLY

Dancing, dancing, zooms the fly;
inside rooms its food to spy.

People shout: 'Get out! Get out!'
But the fly, it heareth nowt!

The fly flies on, dancing, dancing,
with its fly face laughing, laughing.

Assiya Khatoon (aged 10)
(Bangladesh and UK)
Translated by Safuran Ara and Debjani Chatterjee

BUTTERFLIES

Butterflies;
Like pieces of torn paper
Strewn into the wind.

N. C. Wickramasinghe
(Sri Lanka)

TO A FEARLESS HEART . . .

To a fearless heart a lion is a sheep;
To a timid heart a deer is a tiger.
If you have no fear, the ocean is a desert;
If you are fearful, there is a crocodile in every wave.

Muhammad Iqbal
(India and Pakistan)
Translated by Mustansir Mir

Muhammad Allama Iqbal (1877–1938) was born at Sialkot, Punjab, which is now in Pakistan. A poet-philosopher, he wrote in Urdu, Persian and English. Iqbal is the national poet of Pakistan.

HELLO MR PYTHON

Hello Mr Python
Curling round a tree
Bet you'd like to make yourself
A dinner out of me.

Can't you change your habits
Crushing people's bones?
I wouldn't like a dinner
That emitted fearful groans.

Spike Milligan (1918–2002)
(UK)

THE JUNGLE

The jungle comes to life at dawn:
Swift cheetahs chase as gazelles race,
Panthers prowl and wild jackals howl,
The peacock's dance dazzles the fowl.

Crocodiles by the riverside,
slide in mud as they wait and hide.
Buffaloes at the waterhole –
Crocodile claims a careless foal.

Rhinos nod and elephants plod.
King cobra hisses death kisses.
Hunting packs and meat on hoof,
In one jungle below one roof.

Asif Ahmed
(Pakistan and UK)

PIGEONS

They embody a consciousness
that shines among light-grey rocks.

In their bodies old stories of flight
repeat themselves, refresh memory.

During the long Indian afternoons
they rest upon our polished floors,

their bodies refracting the warmth
of close contact, their small heads

forming a community of wisdom.
A picture of extreme importance is seen –

a picture that comprehends everything,
all things contemporary and long past.

But before our eyes gain their fixed look
and our envy its pale green stare,

they rise up, holy and untouched, to disappear among
a history of mocking wings, in the accepting sky.

Bibhu Padi
(India)

THE OWL'S LOVE SONG

Said the Owl to his mate, 'O my peach,
How sweet, I aver, is your screech!
Each squawk that your mandibles utter
Reduces my heart to a flutter,
The croaking crescendos you capture
Inspire me with fathomless rapture!
Your tremolo flows all a-quiver,
The trees grow ecstatic and shiver,
And O what an intricate tangle
Of titters you mix and you mangle!
All torment and trembling and sorrow,
Despond for the past and the morrow,
The pit-a-pat play of my tensions,
Are drowned by your dulcet inventions.
Such strains from your sweet pout leaping
Unman me with measureless weeping!'

Sukumar Ray
(India)
Translated by Sukanta Chaudhuri

Writer, illustrator, scientist and social reformer, Sukumar Ray
(1887–1923) is best known for his 'nonsense' poetry for children.

THE BIRD FEEDER

Daughter,
your absence is woven
into giant wall tapestries
but I cannot unearth
your footprints.

A song comes from the empty
birdfeeder creaking in the wind,
as orphans, four rice grains,
wait for a stray bird.

Here we played
for hours the ritual of feeding and
singing that gave you a setting
for the future. I must learn that
letting go can also mean love.

I clean the tarnished tray,
put fresh grains of rice
and wait for the stray bird.

Padmaja Rao
(India and UK)

SNAKES ALIVE!

Snakes
    are slimy
        and scaly too.
    I like snakes
as much as you!
    Snakes slither
        in the grass.
    Snakes can climb
up walls and slide
    down too.
        Some snakes can be
poisonous, so you
    better watch out
        before you
    get poisoned.
Some snakes are cobras
    and can dance.
        Some snakes are pythons
    and they squeeze you
to death.
    Some snakes are rattlers
        and have rattles
    on their sneaky
      snaky
   tails.

Buphinder Singh Binning (aged 9) and
Debjani Chatterjee
(India and UK)

THE SSSSNAKE HOTEL

An Indian python will welcome you
to the Ssssnake hotel.
As he finds your keys he'll maybe enquire
if you're feeling well.
And he'll say that he hopes
you survive the night,
that you sleep without screaming
and don't die of fright
at the Ssssnake hotel.

There's an anaconda that likes to wander
the corridors at night,
and a boa that will lower itself on to guests
as they search for the light.
And if, by chance, you like awake
and nearby something hisses,
I warn you now, you're about to be covered
with tiny vipery kisses,
at the Ssssnake hotel.

And should you hear a chorus of groans
coming from the room next door,
and the python cracking someone's bones,
please don't go out and explore.
Just ignore all the screams
and the strangled yells
when you spend a weekend
at the Ssssnake hotel.

Brian Moses
(UK)

Anaconda: a large non-poisonous snake. The name originates
from the Sinhala word henakandaya for a snake in Sri Lanka.
Vipery: suggestive of vipers or poisononous snakes.

A QUESTION OF A SNAKE

King
Cobra in your
black and gold, But is your
Heart so stony cold? Or do
You cry what evil score
Dubbed you uncaring
carnivore? When you
kiss your victimss
neck, Do tears
fall in sad
regret
that
your
only
form
of greeting
is taste to see
if it's worth eating.
As in dance you
spread your hood,
Do you feeeeeel
misunderstood?
When victim
frozen
stiff
with
fear,
Feeelss   ?
deathss   e
the one   n
caresss   What venom   o
you   you eat?   Is it   l
share,   those   that   a
Slipping   ponder   you   and
ssoftly   Do you   own? hated
into sleep   Living

Sue Hardy-Dawson
(UK)

85

UNDER THE ALLIGATOR'S SKIN

Above, in that plain where the water meets the sky,
Where I lay my head, looking for you,
Then retreat below that roof when you come,
Afraid you will catch me, and like me too.

And beyond, where both meet the shore,
Where you come looking for me,
Then retreat when you see me,
Afraid I will catch you, and like you too.

Ravi Vangadam
(India and USA)

THE SOUND

A skyful of stars
blinked silent messages.
No moon glistened the leaves
of the sleeping jungle
where a thousand small creatures
curled at rest.

Then . . . the Sound –
huge as mountains
it cracked the stillness,
trampled the forest floor
with its trumpeting . . .

Elephant!

Ruth Dalton
(UK)

HOW TO TREAT
AN ELEPHANT

A zoo is a silly place to call home
and Nellie is a silly name for any elephant
her real name was Savinamay, an ancient name
from a time long ago that meant wondering child of
  love
a time when all animals talked and hyenas laughed at
  all jokes
and all crocodiles were smiling, carrot-eating
  vegetarians
a time when you could sleep at night safe under the
  stars
and the warm evening breeze would carry you high
to the snow-capped mountain tops, where a fingertip
touch of coldness would awake you, for you to look
below to see the whole wide world and its
  wonderment
through starry eyes, and know that the only true
  magic
and way to treat anyone is with love.

Ian Wilson
(UK)

HIGH TIME

Black elephants
jazz dancing
gold and red
grin
I imagine
they wave
as they pass the window
of my third floor flat
just in case they are
I wave back.

Shamshad Khan
(Pakistan and UK)

EXTREMELY ELEGANT ELEPHANTS

Extremely elegant elephants eat
fruit for dinner and trees for sweets,
polish the nails on their dainty feet,
enjoy the jungle and city streets.

Extremely elegant elephants expect
true honesty and great respect,
will ponder deeply and reflect,
can wash their ears behind their necks.

Extremely elegant elephants encourage
nose-drinking even when its porridge,
ecological gatherings whilst they forage,
have few bad habits you can't discourage.

Extremely elegant elephants' eyes
express their joy at being surprised,
though most aren't all that fond of mice,
and show off when they exercise.

Extremely elegant elephants eat
fruit for dinner and trees for sweets,
polish the nails on their dainty feet,
enjoy the jungle and city streets.

Sue Hardy-Dawson
(UK)

CAT

Again and again through the day
I meet a cat.
In the tree's shade, in the sun, in the crowding brown
    leaves.
After the success of a few fish bones
Or inside a skeleton of white earth
I find it, as absorbed in the purring
Of its heart as a bee.
Still it sharpens its claws on the gulmohar tree
And follows the sun all day long.

Now I see it and then it is gone,
Losing itself somewhere.
On the autumn evening I have watched it play,
Stroking the soft body of the saffron sun
With a white paw. Then it caught
The darkness in paws like small balls
And scattered it all over the earth.

Jibananda Das
(India)
Translated by Lila Ray

Jibananda Das (1899–1954) was a well-known poet writing in
Bengali.
Gulmohar: this tree with its vivid blossoms is also called Flame
of the Forest.

LOOK AT THE CLOUD-CAT . . .

Look at the cloud-cat, lapping there on high
With lightning tongue the moon-milk from the sky!

Yogeśvara (c. AD 700–800)
(India)
Translated by Debjani Chatterjee

CHIMPANZEE

It's great to be a chimpanzee
Swinging through the trees
And if we can't find nuts to eat
We munch each other's fleas!

Giles Andreae

(UK)

JEWELS

The wild peacocks of Rajasthan
are sapphires on the grassy banks
and skulk along unseen, they think,
between the village and the tanks.

The wild peahens of Rajasthan
are milkstones on the grassy banks,
and also skulk along in flocks,
for which we give eternal thanks.

Simon Fletcher
(UK)

The peacock is the national bird of India.
Rajasthan: a state in India that is famous for its colourful and
romantic history and legends.
Sapphires and milkstones: blue and white precious stones.

PRIDE SHOT

Lions were posing for cute pictures.
'Where's your pride?' roared the jungle hectors.
　　But the pride shook their manes:
　　　'Our main concern remains
That our tales be shot, so no lectures!'

Debjani Chatterjee
(India and UK)

Pride: 'self-respect' and also 'a company of lions'.

FLAVOURS OF ASIA

Poems About Food and Dress

THE PICNIC

My best friend and I are two grains of rice
we're twins, alike as two earrings
swing our hands like birds in flight
two pendants on a single chain.

We eat on her balcony in the sun
I put up my umbrella for shade
cars moan in the traffic jam below
flat roofs stretch away.

Just like India, I tell her.
Cream cheese tucked into chapattis
ladies fingers peep through white bread
golden bracelets of *jilebees*.

My friend's mum comes to the door.
Put down your umbrella, she says to me
You'll make it rain, you stupid girl.
I close my umbrella, fold its wings.

We don't talk about her mum
but hold hands through the dusty streets
my brown fingers, her white ones
and our secrets captured in between.

Selina Rodrigues
(Anglo-Indian and UK)

Jilebees: fried syrupy sweets.

FLAVOURS OF ASIA

Smell the sizzle:
    the flavours of Asia unfurled
    are a heavenly favour to the world!

Just delight in:
    Bengal potatoes well diced,
    the air of curry smell spiced,
    the feel of breaking bhaji as it's munched,
    the papery sound of poppadoms crunched.

Everyone knows:
    to eat vindaloo
    is good for you!
    Italians who like pasta
    slurp it much too fasta.

I have to say:
    I am a fan of chapatti and nan –
    for dinner I'll travel to Pakistan.
    Salsa from Spain may dance off the plate,
    but it's not the food I appreciate.

Everyone knows:
    to eat vindaloo
    is *better* for you!
    How can Scot's porridge oats
    compete for taste bud votes?

You may say that:
   in England there's marmalade on toast
   but it can't compare with Asia's boast!
   Eat mild or hot curries,
   my hearties – *no* worries!

Everyone knows:
   to eat vindaloo
   is good for you!
   Tuck into hot carrot halwa
   and mouth-watering *kheer kamla*.

Take it from me:
   you need not be from India
   to adore tikka masala.
   You need not be Pakistani
   to *love* chicken biriani.

Everyone knows:
   to eat vindaloo
   is good for you!
   And chilli beans from Nepal
   and coriander in dhal.

Let us agree:
    this balti desire
    sets throats on fire,
    keeps all germs at bay
    both night and day!

Smell the sizzle:
    the flavours of Asia unfurled
    are an exotic favour to the world!

Kendric Ross
(UK)

Bhaji: fried onions or other vegetables.
Poppadoms: thin and crispy savouries, usually eaten as a starter.
Vindaloo: a hot and sour curry.
Chapatti and nan: Indian bread.
Salsa: a Latin-American dance and music.
Halwa: a sweet dish.
Kheer kamla: a sweet dish made with condensed milk and oranges.
Tikka masala: a combination of spices for a curry.
Biriani: a rice dish cooked with chicken or other meat.
Nepal: a Hindu kingdom north of India.
Coriander: a popular South Asian herb.
Dhal: a lentil soup from South Asia.
Balti: food cooked and served in a karahi or Indian wok.

INDIAN COOKING

The bottom of the pan was a palette –
paprika, cayenne, dhania
haldi, heaped like powder-paints.

Melted ghee made lakes, golden rivers.
The keema frying, my mother waited
for the fat to bubble to the surface.

Friends brought silver-leaf.
I dropped it on khir –
special rice pudding for parties.

I tasted the landscape, customs
of my father's country –
its fever on biting a chilli.

Moniza Alvi
(Pakistan and UK)

Dhania: coriander.
Haldi: turmeric.
Keema: minced meat.
Khir: condensed sweet milk.

FOR STARTERS

For Starters

love
Indian, Chinese
And Italian too.

Race is
Not an issue
With me

So long as
The service
And food

Are good.

Hamid Shami
(Pakistan and Scotland)

THE NOODLE EATER

I am a noodle eater,
I eat them in the night,
I eat them by the basketful
and give my dad a fright.

I eat them dry,
I eat them wet,
I eat them upside down.
And best of all I eat them with
an eyebrow-meeting frown.

Chrissie Gittins
(UK)

I ROLLED THEM IN TURMERIC . . .

I rolled them in turmeric, cumin, and spice,
With masses of pepper to make them taste nice:
In lashings of sesame oil I then fried 'em –
The pungency curled up my tongue when I tried 'em:
I neglected to wash, and got down to the dish,
and I swallowed that curry of nice little fish.

Anon.
(India)
Translated

This is a translation of a classical Sanskrit poem found in *The Subhâsitararatnakosa* or *A Treasury of Fine Verses* compiled by Vidyâkara at the end of the eleventh century.

A HOT SPELL

With my special spell,
I can make a huge curry
vanish. It's magic.

David Bateman
(UK)

MY SARI

Saris hang on the washing line:
a rainbow in our neighbourhood.
This little orange one is mine,
it has a mango leaf design.
I wear it as a Rani would.
It wraps around me like sunshine,
it ripples silky down my spine,
and I stand tall and feel so good.

Debjani Chatterjee
(India and UK)

Rani: an Indian queen.

TARTAN AND TURBAN

Give me your tartan
And I will wear it with
The spirit of my race.
I can defend your borders
As I did the Punjab's
In long war-torn days.

I will wear your tartan
With the pride and strength
Of my history
And tribe.
I will weave in its pattern
The breadth and length
Of five rivers that subscribed
To my wealth, which I will now
Lend to your tartan
And make it mine – this new
Sight tartan, willing to
Blend with my Sikh turban
At my journey's end.

Bashabi Fraser
(India and UK)

Five rivers: a reference to the Punjab, which is the land of five rivers and the home of Sikhism. Sikhs keep long hair and wear a turban to keep it in check.

DUPATTA

It tastes like
The essence of Asia.
It smells like
The soil of Punjab.
It feels like
The warmth from the cold,
Cosy and nice.
It looks like
A small breeze blowing
Over a still sea.

Nasima Masood
(Pakistan and UK)

Dupatta: a long scarf.

MUSLIM GIRL AT
THE BUS STOP

Muslim girl at the bus stop
wearing hejab and headphones,

full-length skirt and colourful top,
respecting Allah and listening to hip-hop,

the fingers of her left hand
click to the beat of the tune,

the fingers of her right hand
adjust the veil, keep it in place,

covering her hair
and perfectly framing her beautiful face.

Thomas McColl
(UK)

Hejab: a cloth covering the head, worn by some Muslim women.

HELPING OUT

Eating sugar cane in my uncle's field,
cut fresh with a machete.

Stringy strands between my teeth.
Sweet heaven in my mouth.

Wiping my chin with the back
of my hand before drenching myself
again with flowing sugar water.

John Siddique
(UK)

Machete: a heavy knife with a broad blade.

MORE THAN I WEAR

(For the young women in the
Asian Women's Resource Association)

A young woman, Asian and British,
I have swallowed the world's rough oyster
  – pearl and all; yes, pearl and all.

I've had hard times and will face worse times,
but my gear is sorted and, sister,
  right now, I'm having a ball!

I move to Indi-pop and bhangra,
dupatta flying from my shoulder –
  angel wings and waterfall.

  The world is my oyster – pearl and all.
  Sister, right now, I'm having a ball!

Dadiji gave me this hand-stitched *chunni*.
Her love flows through it like a river,
  and I float tall – I float tall.

  The world is my oyster – pearl and all.
  Sister, right now, I'm having a ball!

I bought myself this denim jacket
and embroidered a lotus flower
   – there's none like it in the mall!

   The world is my oyster – pearl and all.
   Sister, right now, I'm having a ball!

My silk *kameez* glows with gold sequins
my satin *salwar* mirrors the hour
   in Halifax and Bengal.

   The world is my oyster – pearl and all.
   Sister, right now, I'm having a ball!

My Doc Martins pack a feisty kick.
I am from Bradford and Jullunder,
   Mirpur, Punjab and Walsall.

   The world is my oyster – pearl and all.
   Sister, right now, I'm having a ball!

More than I wear, I'm Asian British!
My clothes are those that eye the future,
with respect for tradition's power.
Sari or jeans, I am the daughter
   of Birmingham and Southall.

The world is my oyster – pearl and all.
Sister, right now, I'm having a ball!
Sister, right now, I'm having a ball!

Debjani Chatterjee
(India and UK)

Bhangra: a vigorous Punjabi folk dance and its music.
Dadiji: Grandmother.
Chunni: a scarf.
Kameez: a tunic.
Salwar: baggy trousers for wearing with a kameez.
Jullunder: a city in the Punjab in India.
Mirpur: a district in Pakistan.

MEHNDI TIME

Festivals and Festivities

MELA MENAGERIE

It was summertime,
the animals were having a mela.
    The elephants cooked
curried pumpkin with tikka masala,
    sun-shy frogs and mice
sheltered under the hood of a cobra,
    bears and cockatoos
swapped couplets in a mini *mushaira*,
    horses and camels
pranced and danced a fantastic bhangra,
    tigers took pot-shot
at juicy papayas for one paisa,
    lions showed off paws
decorated with delicate henna,
    donkeys for a laugh
crowned Mule their day-long Maharaja,
    pelicans swallowed
swords with mango chutney and paratha,
    Sindbad's ship sailed in
on waves of dolphin abracadabra,
    monkeys built bridges
recalling how they once helped Prince Rama,
    while Ali Baba
and forty rooks acted out life's drama.
    It was summertime,
the animals were having a mela.

Debjani Chatterjee
(India and UK)

Mushaira: Urdu word for a gathering of poets.

Mela: a South Asian fair, a periodical festive market place.

Paratha: a kind of fried bread.

Paisa: a coin used in India, Bangladesh, Pakistan and Nepal.

Chutney: a pungent relish made from fruit, vinegar, spices and herbs. The word 'chutney' has come into English from Hindi.

EID SONG

Ramadan's over . . .
   Eid Mubarak!
A month has passed . . .
   Eid Mubarak!
We've done our best . . .
   Eid Mubarak!
To keep the fast . . .
   Eid Mubarak!
Now it's time . . .
   Eid Mubarak!
To have some fun . . .
   Eid Mubarak!
Come and visit . . .
   Eid Mubarak!
The feast's begun!

Tony Langham
(UK)

Ramadan: Muslim month of fasting. The Koran was revealed during this time.
Eid: Muslim festival. There are several Eid festivals but the main one is Eid Al-Fittr which comes at the end of Ramadan.
Mubarak: congratulations.

JOYS OF RAMZAN

In Ramzan we please Allah,
We please Allah.
Offer *Namaz* and *Jummah*.

Shaitan is chained
Blessings gained
Vices forbidden
Sins forgiven.

Wings spread
Angels descend
Enfold us under
Realms of wonder:

They join us in daily routine
Rise early for *Sehri* cuisine
Five prayers and breaking the fast
Late to bed, midnight past.

In Ramzan we please Allah,
We please Allah.
Offer *Namaz* and *Jummah*.

To forget hunger,
We do *Zikker*, think of others:
Friends and neighbours.

Feasts are shared –
All our favourites: tikka masala
Spring rolls and potato phulkah

In Ramzan we please Allah,
We please Allah.
Offer *Namaz* and *Jummah*.

Good will ignites
Everyone unites
Invitations ring for breaking fast
Doors are opened to the outcast

We feel proud at having fasted
Made sacrifices, and having lasted
Made our lives a little harder
Seeking peace for the here and the hereafter

Radio voices, charity appeals,
Making gifts is no big deal.
Daddies empty their pockets
And hand over wallets
Mummies, their gold bracelets

Children caress their favourite toys
As they say goodbye for strangers' joys.
With bodies leaner,
the spirit's cleaner.

In caring, sharing we please Allah,
Please Allah
Offer *Namaz* and *Jummah*.

Sitara Khan
(Pakistan and UK)

Shaitan: Satan.

Ramzan: Urdu word for Ramadan, the month when the Koran was revealed.

Namaz: Urdu and Persian word for the formal five daily prayers offered by Muslims.

Jummah: Friday prayer for Muslims.

Sehri: an early morning prayer.

Zikker: Arabic term for chanting God's name in prayer.

Tikka masala, spring rolls and potato phulkah: savoury dishes.

RAMADAN

The moon that once was full, ripe and golden,
Wasted away, thin as the rind of a melon,
Like those poor whom sudden ill fortune
Has wasted away like a waning moon.

Like the generous who leave behind
All that was selfish and unkind,
The moon comes out of the tent of the night
And finds its way with a lamp of light.

The lamp of the moon is relit
And the hungry and thirsty
In the desert or the city
Make a feast to welcome it.

Stanley Cook
(UK)

119

DIWALI

Diwali lamps are twinkling, twinkling
In the sky and in our homes and hearts.
We welcome all with cheery greetings
And sweets and patterned *rangoli* art.
Lakshmi flies upon her owl tonight;
Incense curls, our future's sparkling bright.

Debjani Chatterjee
(India and UK)

Rangoli: patterns drawn at the entrance to a home to welcome
visitors.
Lakshmi: the Hindu Goddess of Wealth and Good Fortune, she
blesses the homes where lamps are lit in her honour at Diwali –
the festival of light.

PALM PRINT

at last it's my turn
with the henna lady

'hold your hand out
please, nice and flat'

excited, I stretch out my palm
whilst she shows me a book filled with patterns

she says I can choose, I pick flowers and leaves
made of beautiful dots

the first drop
on my finger tip
pine forest fresh
and cold to the bone

she presses the cone to my finger
dark mud oozes in a thin line from within

she tickles and trickles
till the pattern is complete

just like the work of jack frost
but in black

then the henna lady tells me to sit
till it's dried

I get a bit fidgety
can't wait all that time

so I start to pick
till the paste flakes off

all the dried bits
finally gone

and even though I knew,
it's still a surprise

orange sunset of flowers
a wild, red henna bouquet
spread out on my hand

Shamshad Khan
(Pakistan and UK)

COME PLAY WITH ME –
IT'S HOLI!

Come play with me
 – it's Holi!

Tell me you won't play
and I'll pelt you anyway
with colours that will stay
with you all day – for today
is Holi!

You are the girl that didn't care
to throw a glance at me.
I am the boy that didn't dare
to ask you to dance with me.

Today I'm out with my gang
drenched with colour, drunk with *bhang*
I am your Krishna come to play
your friends – my *Gopis* who will spray
me with *abir*, for today
is Holi!

And you my Radha cannot stay inside.
The spring sky calls, come play outside
with coloured water – do not hide –
for today is Holi!

Upset the coloured powder mounds
in clouds of purple, pink and green,
let your *chunni* swirl around,
join your bangled hands with hand.

It's true I do not have a flute
or peacock feathers on my head;
I only know the Bombay hits
and have a cricket cap instead,
which I will throw at your feet
and dance the *bhangra* to the beat
as we sway our hips today
to the *dholki*'s frenzied beat . . .

Rhythmic shoulders, clapping hands,
faces streaked, coloured strands,
saris sprayed, *kurtas* stained
friends doused, strangers drained
from pistons, buckets, balconies,
street corners, terraces and trees –
till the wall you try to build
crumbles down against my will

– I'll touch your cheeks and arms
with colour which disarms
you for one day
of abandon –
so let us play
as Radha-Krishna – for today
is Holi!

Bashabi Fraser
(India and UK)

Holi: Hindu spring festival of colours.
Bhang: an alcoholic drink that is drunk at Holi. It is made with
milk, nuts and herbs.
Krishna: a popular god who has a peacock feather in his hair
and plays the flute enchantingly. He loved to dance with the
Gopis or milkmaids, chief among whom was his sweetheart
Radha.
Abir: the coloured powder with which Holi is played.
Bhangra: a Punjabi folk dance.
Dholki: a kind of drum.
Kurtas: long tunics worn in India and Pakistan.

A CARD FOR ME MOM

It is Mother's Day tomorrow
and the shops are full of wonderful things –
candles, picture-frames, pot-pourri in glass dishes,
but I only have money for a card, and there are dozens –
cards with teddies and roses, cards with moms
in dresses, with gold and red hair and blue eyes.
None of them look like me Mom.
If there was just one card to show
Mom with her gold necklace, bangles and earrings,
reminding me of her soft jingle-jangle as she washes
the curry pots or mixes the dough for rotis and nans,
in her silk kameezes and chiffon chunnies – one mom
with long black hair and flashing dark eyes
who looks more like me Mom!

Bashabi Fraser
(India and UK)

MEHNDI TIME

(To welcome Tulika to our family)

The love of family and friends –
at *mehndi* time, at *mehndi* time –
the joy of stories and laughter –
at *mehndi* time, at *mehndi* time,
embrace me like a magic ring
as they clap their hands and sing:

May the new bride bring a blessing,
mehndi *magic mark her wedding.*
With designs – intricate and neat –
we'll decorate her hands and feet.

With bright lines of ochre colour –
at *mehndi* time, at *mehndi* time –
my sisters pattern loving warmth –
at *mehndi* time, at *mehndi* time.
In life my journey may be far
as I pursue my *mehndi* star.

Painted shells and lotus flowers
decorate these happy hours.
Rich mango leaves and tree of life –
love's anchors for our new-wed wife.

I will nourish tradition's fruit
  at *mehndi* time, at *mehndi* time.
What memories I will cherish –
  of *mehndi* time, of *mehndi* time!
Like *mehndi* bushes, cool and green,
may *mehndi* make my life serene.

Her feet are tinted coral-rose,
her hands are jewels in repose.
May her new life flow with blessing,
mehndi *magic mark her wedding.*

It's *mehndi* time, it's *mehndi* time . . .

Debjani Chatterjee
(India and UK)

Mehndi: henna.

THE NEW GAVASKAR

Poems About Work, School and Play

BIG SISTER

They dig by the river for bricklaying –
labourers from the west country. Their little girl
keeps scampering to the ghat. Such scrubbing and
   scouring
of pots and pans and dishes! Comes running
a hundred times a day, brass bangles jangling
clang clang against the brass plates she cleans.
So busy all day! Her little brother,
bald, mud-daubed, not a stitch on his limbs,
follows her like a pet, patiently sits
on the high bank, as Big Sister commands.
Plates against her left side, a full pitcher on her head,
the girl goes back, the child's hand in her right hand.
A surrogate of her mother,
bent under her work-load, such a wee Big Sister!

Rabindranath Tagore
(India)
Translated by Ketaki Kushari Dyson

Ghat: river bank

ENGLISH LITERATURE – GCE

'Two dozen pupils
Dissect the set texts
Relentless hands
Ripping apart the delicate flowers
Petal by petal
To learn
How to understand beauty.'

Savitri Hensman
(India and UK)

THE NEW GAVASKAR

I have pinned a poster
Of Sunil Gavaskar
In my bedroom.
I keep all his scores.
I practise his stance
At the batting crease
Behind closed doors.
But they won't let me in
The school cricket team.

I play with my brothers, cousins –
We make up just seven.
On Sunday mornings
We gather our battered ball,
A bat, stumps, odd pad or two
And then march down
The sleepy Calcutta lane
To our pitch – a small
Half-grass half-mud field.

We play like shadows
In the mist. And shout 'Catch it',
'How's that'. Swap pad or
Bat. All of us chase the ball
when hit in case it is lost.
One day it hits my thumb.
I don't cry then or in Casualty.
Later I show my mates the old nail
Like a reserved ticket to fame.

I know my school misses me –
The new Gavaskar for the MCC.

Asit Maitra
(India and UK)

Sunil Gavaskar: an Indian cricket hero.
MCC: Maitra Cricket Club.

SCHOOLYARD
'National Colours'

The teams picked and lined-up in rank,
we jogged on to the school football pitch
like iambs on a sonnet's green rectangle,
limbering-up for the big metre.
There we were, high with the fresh
juice of adolescence in our shorts –
the keen ones, jittering like wound-up
clockwork toys, in Scotland strips;
my kit from *What Every Woman Wants*.

The rhythm of the game settled itself
as the ball was passed along the wing
in an a-b-a-b rhyming scheme

Irfan Merchant
(India and UK)

Iambs: a metrical foot in a poem that has an unstressed syllable
followed by a stressed syllable.
Sonnet: a fourteen-line poem, usually in iambic pentameter.
Metre: the measured rhythm that is characteristic of poetry.
Adolescence: youth.

Irfan Merchant (b. 1973) was born in Liverpool of Indian descent
and brought up in Scotland.

A SKIPPING GAME

Skip one and skip two
Chicken korma with pilau.
Skip three and skip four
Mamma's pizza to your door.
Skip five and skip six
Chinese noodles with chopsticks.
Skip seven and skip eight
Fish 'n' chips on a paper plate.
Skip nine and skip ten
I'll eat out and you'll eat in!

Bashabi Fraser
(India and UK))

(Two children swing a skipping rope. A third child skips in the middle – then goes out to let the next one in.)

135

THE REMOVE

The Sikh from Ambala in East Punjab,
India, formerly in the British Empire,
the Muslim from Sialkot in West Punjab,
Pakistan, formerly British India,
the Sikh boy and the Muslim boy are two
of twenty such Sikhs and Muslims
from East Punjab and West Punjab, which
formerly were the Punjab,
standing together in assembly, fearfully
miming the words of a Christian hymn.

Later, their firework voices explode
in Punjabi until Mr Iqbal –
which can be a Sikh name or a Muslim name,
Mohammed Iqbal or Iqbal *Singh* –
who comes from Jullundur in East Punjab
but near enough to the border to be almost
West Punjab, who is a specialist in
the archaic intonations of the Raj,
until the three-piece-suited Mr Iqbal
gives a stiff-collared voice to his
Punjabi command to shut their thick wet
lips on the scattering sparks of their
white Secondary Modern teeth.

Mr Iqbal has come to London to teach
English to Punjabi Sikhs and Muslims
and has pinned up in his class pictures
of Gandhi and Jinnah, Nehru and Ayub

in case the parents come to ask in Punjabi
how the kids are doing in English.

And so: twenty years after
the Union Jack came down on Delhi
and the Punjabi became East Punjab and
West Punjab and the Sikhs did not like it
and the Muslims did not like the Sikhs
not liking it and they killed each other
not by the hundred nor by the thousand
but by the hundred thousand, here then
is Mr Iqbal with his remove class of
twenty Punjabis, some Sikh and some Muslim,
in a Secondary Modern School in London,
all of them trying to learn English.

Back home the fastidious guardians of freedom,
the Sikh army and the Muslim army, convinced
that East is East and West is West etcetera,
periodically accuse each other of aggression.

Zulfikar Ghose
(Pakistan, UK and USA)

Jinnah, Nehru and Ayub: M. A. Jinnah (1876–1948), also called
Qaid-e-Azam – meaning 'Leader of the nation' – was Pakistan's
founding father. Jawaharlal Nehru (1889–1964) was India's first
Prime Minister. Ayub Khan (1907–74) was Pakistan's President
in the 1960s.
Remove class: class of students who are 'removed' from the
main class.

KHITISH

Hurtling into the clutter-room
whose door hung loose on its hinges,
I knocked against him coming out,
barefoot and with lungi folded
above the knees. Khitish held me
with his bony grip and brown eyes,
our lanky servant who was king
of the fish ponds and muddy swamps,
the hero who opened the gates
to adventure. I looked at him
expectantly, for he always
gave me keys that unlock treasures
to scatter in my clutter-room.
From out his pocket a carved top
of sal wood with a string spiralled
tight around it, transferred itself
to my greedy hands. 'All it wants
is a lick of paint,' said Khitish,
'then watch it spin, little sister.'
I twirled it straight away, pulling
back the string with all the flourish
of some conjuror whisking off
a table cloth to leave behind
crockery and cutlery set
in immaculate arrangement.

'Brilliant!' I breathed, giving him
my unstinted admiration.

Debjani Chatterjee
(India and UK)

Khitish: a Bengali name.
Lungi: a light cloth wrap worn by men and tied at the waist.
Sal: a tree prized in South Asia for its wood.
Immaculate: perfect.
Unstinted: abundant.

FROM SYLHET TO SHEFFIELD

My village in Sylhet has many streams.
Small and friendly, they invited our play;
each day after school I'd go with my friends,
we'd splash in the waters and sing and shout.
I thought this life would go on forever.

Then my family flew across the seas.
Everything was strange in a foreign land:
the language, the food, the weather, the school.
My world was upside down and I'd rush home
each day after school. I longed to fly back.

Sheffield was so large – I longed to escape
but its small and friendly streams spoke of home.
With my sisters and brothers I grew up
in this city, learned English and made friends.
Now our children play beside the canal.

Mina Begum
(Bangladesh and UK)

Sylhet: a hilly district in northern Bangladesh. Its capital is also
called Sylhet.

AMMA, I LIKE SCHOOL

Amma, I like school,
It is such fun,
We play most of the time
And sing songs in French.
Amma, finger-painting is such fun
So many bright bright colours
And we can use all we want.
Amma, if a crayon breaks
You can just throw it away
And take a new one!
Ma, you think you could change my name
To Jim or David or something?
Amma, I love recess time.
Did you see the tyres?
The tyres tied together?
I can climb up
And sit inside and swing
Such fun.
When winter comes
I'll turn less brown
Won't I, Ma?
It would be nice to be
Like everyone else, you know?

Uma Parameswaran
(India and Canada)

SRI LANKAN SCHOOLROOM

Traipsing across sports grounds
picked clean by equator sun
we visit my father's school:
long-distance callers
at the museum of memory.

My father points out the places
where, giggling, his friends once sat,
names that belong to old men
in London and Toronto now,
names that could barely fit behind these desks.

His teacher remains unchanged.
paper-dry voice crackling
he dictates the rites of duty and decorum,
the triumph of courtesy and reason
over the casual accident of race.

It is Jaffna, 1983.
It is one day in a long, hot summer.
It is one day, seconds away from war,
and, decades from now,
this is all that I'll remember
of that visit to that country:
the sand dust in the air,
the sun bleaching dry the shutters
and the walls, empty of pictures,
not even a map of the world.

Pireeni Sundaralingam
(Sri Lanka and USA)

Jaffna: a city and peninsula in northern Sri Lanka, mostly popu-
lated by Tamils. As the stronghold of militant Tamil groups
fighting the Sri Lankan army, Jaffna has suffered much destruc-
tion in modern times.
1983: the Liberation Tigers of Tamil Eelam began their war for
independence.

HOLIDAY

In the lap of clouds is the sun's laughter,
   the storm has gone away.
Hey, today is our holiday, brother,
   today is our holiday!
I can't think what we should do,
   in which forest can we lose our way?
In which field shall we run about,
   all of us friends together?
Hey, today is our holiday, brother,
   today is our holiday!

Rabindranath Tagore
(India)
Translated by Debjani Chatterjee

OF TONGUES AND AMAZONS

Elocution class at the convent
was a heart-thumping ordeal for us 'native' girls.
Miss Rhondo would stride in,
a dark and miniscule dinosaur
who froze the grey matter in our brains
and delivered a vicious lockjaw
to cause our tongues to slither and stutter,
and our sweaty red-socked feet to shuffle
in white-chalked canvas shoes.
We rose in uniform drudgery
and greeted her with a singsong
'Good afternoon, Miss Rhondo' of shabby hypocrisy.
It irked her from the start
and she'd have us practise standing up
and sitting down with pathetic
time-wasting rows of 'Good afternoon'.
The crowd-saving distraction of 'the Mexican wave'
was not yet invented, but ripples of frustration
erupted and died.

Gita was surely a native too, but with attitude –
the one we looked up to with horror
and mounting excitement. No one knew
what she'd do on any given day
to break the regimented monotony.
She was a dusky native, but not like any of us;
she was an Amazon – tall and strong,
hockey captain of our class.
'How dare you, Girl!' Miss Rhondo
thundered. 'You disgust me

with your native English.' But Gita's eyes
would dance mischief as she tossed
plump pigtails in the air.
She was always punished but she didn't care.

Amazons were from another world.
They belonged with Greek myths,
opium-eating Quincy's essays
and Lamb's *Tales from Shakespeare*.
In Miss Rhondo's elocution class
our Babu English weighed us down
with centuries of mangling
by sepoys and government clerks,
and we mutinied without meaning to.
Our wilting tongues, like orphaned Oliver,
asked for more. Miss Rhondo rattled
the marbles of sarcasm in our Indian mouths
with native tongues colliding:
Bengali, Punjabi, Sindhi, Tamil, Gujarati . . .
tongues that won us punishment
when overheard on the playground.
'Please, Sister Katherine, Usha used Hindi
five times today.' 'Kamala is cursing
in Punjabi, Mother.' Only the mother tongue
knows the enchantment of cursing.
And how can we tell a friend a story
that does not end: '*Amar golpoti phurolo
– noté gaachhti murolo . . .*'?
We ratted on each other like Nazi collaborators
and strangled our ancestral tongues
till they rose to haunt us in nightmares.

I was an 'assassin of the Queen's language',
Miss Rhondo said. There was blood
on my barbarous tongue. I looked at it
in the mirror – it was a 'native' tongue
that I had to use as a pummelling bag;
I had to tongue-punch it daily.
It was the protean dough of roti
for routine squeezing and thumping,
the gum that had to be sucked
and chewed and blown up into a bubble,
like igniting a hydrogen bomb.
Do not ask me which is more my own –
I shape the tongue as best I can
and language made me.

Gita was one of us 'natives', and yet one of a kind.
One summer's day with the ceiling fan blowing
Miss Rhondo's hot words around the room,
our tongues wilted, browbeaten into grinding
    submission.
Then Gita whistled! How she whistled!
No lady ever did that.
But Gita didn't care to be a lady and we knew
that Amazons live by different rules.
Miss Rhondo could not believe her ears.
'Who made that dreadful noise?' she asked
and we all knew but no one snitched.
She punished us all – we stood on benches,
holding up our schoolbags and feeling fools,
though for once we didn't care.
Honestas ante honores – 'honesty first, then glory',
Miss Rhondo reminded us. Our national motto

said it too in a still more ancient tongue:
Satyameva jayaté – 'Truth triumphs'.
The truth was that Gita shrugged her shoulders
and we decided to join her that day
– we couldn't do what she had done
– we all aspired to ladyhood
– but we could join her for just one lesson
in standing on the benches, we would all
be punished as natives together,
though our mutiny could not last.
Gita, we knew, was an Amazon;
while we could only pretend,
she lived by other rules.

Debjani Chatterjee
(India and UK)

Opium-eating Quincy: Thomas De Quincy (1785–1859) was an essayist who wrote Confessions of an Opium-Eater.

Lamb's *Tales from Shakespeare:* Charles Lamb (1775–1834) was a writer whose story versions of Shakespeare's plays became very popular.

Babu English: abusive term for Indian English.

Sepoys: native Indian soldiers in the British army in India.

'Amar golpoti phurolo – noté gaachhti murolo . . .': literally 'My tale has ended – the plant has wilted', this is the beginning of a nonsensical rhyme that traditionally ends a Bengali folktale.

Honestas ante honores: Latin motto meaning 'honesty first, then glory'.

Satyameva jayaté: Sanskrit expression meaning 'Truth triumphs', it is India's national motto.

MOTHER TONGUE

Mind Your Language

MOTHER TONGUE

Yes,
I speak
Fluent
Urdu
But
In my dreams
I bawl,
Curse
And swear
In the
Queen's
English.

Hamid Shami
(Pakistan and UK)

A LITTLE BIT DIFFERENT –
A LITTLE BIT THE SAME

the way my mother speaks
is a little bit different
she speaks to me in urdu

the way my mother baths me
is a little bit different
she pours on water a bucket or two

the way my mother dresses
is a little bit different
she wears baggy shalwaar and a flowery chemise

but the way my mother loves me
is just the same way
your mum loves you
with a kiss and a cuddle and a tight, tight squeeze

Shamshad Khan
(Pakistan and UK)

Urdu: the national language of Pakistan, it is also one of India's
northern languages.
Shalwaar: also 'salwar', baggy trousers.
Chemise: tunic.

'ERE SHE SAID

'Ere, she said,
Her fag hanging out of her mouth,
Dropping both ash and H's.
'Ere, she said,
Was you born 'ere?
Only you speak very good English.
Where d'ya come from then?
Africa?

Only askin' cos what's 'er name come from there
But she ain't your colouring,
She's darker, much darker
Than you.

And do ya eat food – like what we do?
Y'know, red meat and Yorkshire Pud?
Only what's 'er name says she don't.
She eats – what d'ya call 'em –
Balls of dough, fried like dumplings.

'Ere, she said. Listen to this.
I've bin wif out 'eat for five weeks,
Just bin on to the Council.
But the man said he couldn't unnerstan' me.
Didn't unnerstan' me accent.
Bleeding Asian weren't he!

Sorry . . . din't mean you.
I mean you're not like the rest of 'em.
Are you?

Gita Bedi
(Kenya and UK)

UNSEATED

The Lord of Lords
the Hindu God Suresh
has settled in Birmingham.

The Health Manager asks,
'Your name – what did you say it was?'

The Lord of Lords spoke under his breath,
'Suresh.'

'I would find it difficult.
I am not trained
to pronounce your name,'
the Manager said.

'You will be known as Jim hereafter.
Do you mind?'

Jim sits down.
Suresh, Lord of Lords,
takes a back seat.

                        Shripati Upadhyaya
                        (India and UK)

Many Indian names, like Suresh ('Lord of Lords'), have mean-
ings that are beautiful and lofty. In this poem Shripati
Upadhyaya describes a true incident that occurred in the
National Health Service where he works as a Clinical
Psychologist.

KOH-I-NOOR

There were words I knew early, like 'bungalow',
'veranda', pyjama', 'chitty', 'doolally',
had been assimilated into English
from one or other subcontinental language;

and those I'd learn of later, such as 'loot'
taken from Bengali when a word
was needed to describe the thing exactly.

Irfan Merchant
(India and UK)

Koh-i-Noor: a fabulous Indian diamond that now ornaments
the British crown jewels. Its name means 'mountain of light'.
Bungalow: a single-storey house. The word came into English from
the Gujarati bangalo or the Hindi bangla meaning 'of Bengal'.
Pyjama: the word came into English from the Hindi word for
baggy trousers, paejama.
Chitty: also chit, this is an Anglo-Indian word for a document,
report or certificate. Chhitti is Hindi for 'letter'.
Doolally: slang for 'mentally unbalanced'. British troops stationed
in the town of Deolali near Bombay while waiting to be shipped
home coined the word to mean 'becoming crazy with boredom'.
Subcontinent: the countries of South Asia, i.e. India, Pakistan,
Bangladesh, Sri Lanka and Nepal.
Loot: stolen valuables. The word came into English from the
Hindi word lut.

Irfan Merchant (b. 1973) was born in Liverpool of Indian descent
and brought up in Scotland.

NICE ADVICE

'Don't use the word NICE!' teacher said,
'add some spice instead.'

So I used the word CURRY,
which is really tasty.

I wrote – 'It was a curry holiday.'
And she crossed it in red.

I used the word GOOD in my next work
And she said that's bad as well.

So when she said my drawing was GOOD,
I asked – 'Is that 0 out of 10?'

Mike Jenkins
(UK)

BENGALI LANGUAGE

We speak in Bengali
We write in Bengali
We see the entire world
Through its green glow

We adorn the minarets of our minds
With its countless flowers
Illuminating the sky

With its light in our hands
We journey across the world
Through its sweet melody
We learn the languages of others

Rabindranath Tagore
(India)
Translated by Anwara Jahan

THE SONG OF HERO HIPPO

I'm the king of the mudpool
The hero of the tadpole
The rollicking, frolicking love of your life.
The fatsome, the wholesome,
    the bodysome, the handsome
Your mission, your passion, your fashion for life.
I'll waddle, I'll dawdle, I'll paddle in mud
I'll meddle, I'll muddle, I'll fuddle-de-dud.
My stump of a rump
My pout of a snout
My blossom of bottom
Will all put to rout
Your Hollywood heroes
Who'll all score zeros
In the ultimate show
Of this gainly Hippo -
Not an ignoramous hippopotamus
But an amorous, glamorous,
hip guy
Whose autograph you're clamorous
to buy.

Bashabi Fraser
(India and UK)

158

BUT I SPEAK ENGLISH
ALREADY

All my sentences finished voice-up like the questions
    it was rude to ask.
Why is there no meat in this mince pie?
or
How many times must you say thank you in a shop?
Why don't words in books mean what I say?

In the corner shop I show off my birthday presents:
New top and leggings – bright turquoise cotton.
I ask 'Do you like my new birthday suit?'
Their laughter tells me I've said something dirty.

Jeanne Ellin
(Anglo-Indian and UK)

FLOODS

How many tears plop into a splash?
How many splashes drip into a dribble?
How many dribbles drool into a trickle?
How many trickles tip into a puddle?
How many puddles spill into a pool?
How many pools ooze into a ditch?
How many ditches drench a stream?
How many streams seep into the Ganges River?
How many rivers rise with the Bay of Bengal's tides?
How many tides team into a flood?
How many floods to fill the land?

How many teacups to empty the Indian Ocean?

C. M. Lee Summerfield
(UK)

Hamid Shami (b. 1969) was born in Pakistan and grew up in Glasgow.

GOODBYE PARTY FOR
MISS PUSHPA T. S.

Friends,
our dear sister
is departing for foreign
in two three days,
and
we are meeting today
to wish her bon voyage.

You are all knowing, friends,
what sweetness is in Miss Pushpa.
I don't mean only external sweetness
but internal sweetness.
Miss Pushpa is smiling and smiling
even for no reason
but simply because she is feeling.

Miss Pushpa is coming
from very high family.
Her father was renowned advocate
in Bulsar or Surat,
I am not remembering now which place.

Surat? Ah, yes,
once only I stayed in Surat
with family members
of my uncle's very old friend –
his wife was cooking nicely . . .
that was long time ago.

Coming back to Miss Pushpa
she is most popular lady
with men also and ladies also.

Whenever I asked her to do anything,
she was saying, 'Just now only
I will do it.' That is showing
good spirit. I am always
appreciating the good spirit.

Pushpa Miss is never saying no
whatever I or anybody is asking
she is always saying yes,
and today she is going
to improve her prospects
and we are wishing her bon voyage.

Now I ask other speakers to speak
and afterwards Miss Pushpa
will do the summing up.

Nissim Ezekiel
(India)

Bulsar and Surat: towns in Gujarat in India.
Nissim Ezekiel was born in 1924 into a Jewish family of
Mumbai. He is India's best-known poet writing in English.

FAIR WEATHER

(An English-as-a-Foreign-Language poem)

Hello friend! I am friendly, yes?
'Is fair weather?' Yes, very much:
sun is equal not-so-hot on all,
rain is ever on you, and me also ever,
cold is very much on all also.
English friend ever talk weather.
I come from sunshine very much –
I not like fair weather, so talk weather never.

Debjani Chatterjee
(India and UK)

163

LANGUAGE FOR SALE

Language is spawned on the island
easily as fish eggs
and yet who is it that speaks?
    that is what counts!

White, Black or native speaker? . . .
and when there is no native,
the immigrants quarrel,
    Babel-like.

Language is to do with money, power
you speak it right,
    you get a job
you speak it wrong,
    it will stick in your throat
like a frog croaking
wrong notes all the time.

The leftovers of the colonists
like stale breath and fungied bread
smells bad,
to grow identity
more than your photo-cards with meaningless numbers,
you want your language
the desire grows like a child in the womb.

The long remembered, half-erased memories of
    lullabies,
of harsh nights dawning out into
terrifying days,
    coolie days
I need a language
a language which would mean what I say
which would unearth my leanings – my nuances
and not drawl dictionary meanings back at me . . .

I want my language!

Shakuntala Hawoldar
(India and Mauritius)

Coolie: an unskilled labourer.

from THE DURBAR
IN THE NORTH

Tamil everywhere
In everything there was Tamil
In those days.

Tamil everywhere
Tamil in everything – it was those days.

Now where and whence is Tamil?
I searched till my eyes grew tired
Wandered till my feet grew weary
Thirsting for Tamil.

Softly like the southern breeze she touched – Mother
    Tamil
Embracing me with gentle hands.

. . .

Arise – here is the Northern Durbar.

Revived I was in Urdu
In Gujarati I toddled
Overjoyed I was in Hindi
Marathi made my hair stand on end
Chivalry flowed in Kannada
Rejoice I did in English
But I saluted in Tamil.

Make your blessings flow, Mother Tamil
May these poets grow
To create such Durbars
As long as these languages live
Long live the mother tongue
Long live Tamil!

Geetha Upadhyaya
(India and UK)

Durbar: a royal court or a ceremonial gathering.

DANCING GANAPATI

Myths and Mysteries

DANCING GANAPATI

Dancing Ganapati, trunk in the air,
we loved you and fed you on milk and sweets,
smeared sandal paste on your marble brow,
decked your pachyderm neck with fresh marigold,
beat on our drums and danced while you stared
with ears fanned out, for we hailed you in joy.
We waved oil lamps and swayed as we sang:
'Dancing Ganapati, trunk in the air,
bless us who worship with milk and sweets.'

We slipped away, ate and drank in your name.
Life was as always: flesh-stoned together,
you were our friend, we knew where you stood.
Dancing Ganapati, trunk in the air,
we drank your milk and savoured your sweets
till the day you chose to take our treats –
we wondered where all the milk had gone,
and stared in disbelief at our old playmate:
dancing Ganapati, trunk in the milk!

Debjani Chatterjee
(India and UK)

Ganapati: also called Ganesh, he is the Hindu god of Wisdom.

THE FIRST RAIN

When I first learned how to write,
first of all I wrote Your name.

I am the pure submission
that shouldered the weight of trust.

I am he of noble name
to whom jinns and angels bowed.

Why did You not hold my hand
when I wandered from the path?

Whatever I gained is Yours,
all I lost was also Yours.

I lived lifelong without You,
yet people say that You were mine.

O Sender of the first rain,
I thirsted for sight of You.

Nasir Kazmi
(India and Pakistan)
Translated by Debjani Chatterjee

Jinns: in Muslim legend, spirits that are capable of assuming
human or animal form.
Nasir Kazmi (1925–72) was born in Ambala in India and migrated
to Pakistan when India became independent and partitioned.

RAIN

When the heavens drenched the earth,
there were those who said that,
rumbling Vedic mantras,
Indra poured down oblations.

Others spoke of Indrani's tears,
showering both joy and sorrow;
or even Indra's winged elephant,
splashing and sporting while bathing.

(Airavata did incline
to ecstatic cleanliness.)
But Indra shook his royal head:
'Sometimes it *is* just rain I send.'

Debjani Chatterjee
(India and UK)

Indra: in Indian mythology he is the King of the gods and causes
thunder and rain. Indra rides on a white winged elephant –
Airavata. Indrani is his Queen.
Vedic mantras: chants from the Vedas, the ancient scriptures of
India.

VISHNU'S EAGLE

A sharp-beaked hunter of the chase,
Nemesis of the serpent race,
He scours the Earth, he straddles space,

Spans the heavens with sturdy wings;
From worlds unseen, in glory brings
On his broad back the King of kings.

Debjani Chatterjee
(India and UK)

THE YETI

'Steep
Is the peak,
But we must keep
Watch for the beast we seek.
I'd give half my life for a peep
At the Yeti, the shaggy abominable freak
Who, I'm convinced, exists, for he steals the sheep
Of the sherpas who live down the valley, by the creek.'
After four months of searching, our leader was ready to weep.
Tired, we encamped that night and, since our prospects were bleak,
Reluctantly decided to pack up and depart after a good night's sleep.
But the next morning when we awoke, our heads swam and knees felt weak
To see all our luggage neatly packed and lying outside on the snow in a heap
With a note attached that said: *Good riddance, snooping monsters*. What a cheek!

Debjani Chatterjee
(India & UK)

A SCRATCH

what is god
and what is stone
the dividing line
if it exists
is very thin
at jejuri
and every other stone
is god or his cousin

there is no crop
other than god
and god is harvested here
around the year
and round the clock
out of the bad earth
and the hard rock

that giant hunk of rock
the size of a bedroom
is khandoba's wife turned to stone
the crack that runs right across
is the scar from his broadsword
he struck her down with
once in a fit of rage
scratch a rock
and a legend springs

Arun Kolatkar
(India)

Jejuri: a pilgrim centre near Pune in Maharashtra, India. A popular annual fair is held there. The popularly worshipped god and goddess in Jejuri are Khandoba and his wife Yalamma. Khandoba, a sword-wielding deity, is a Maharashtian version of the god Shiva.

LIZARD CHANT

If a lizard croaked on one's head
thrice, then one would be a king.
(an old saying)

1

The lizard sped across the ceiling,
and unexpectedly, fell on my head.

I heard it croak, feebly, then again, and
before the third one, I had a cardiac arrest.

Years later, when I was in China,
I saw the same lizard, dead, fried, being sold

on the savoury stands at a local market.
I bought it, took it along, and

while aboard the ship returning home,
threw it overboard.

2

Back home, I saw the same lizard again.
Its rind shrivelled, but wet

after a transoceanic swim.
I was reminded of what I once

heard, about a lizard's fall.
I saw it speeding across the ceiling

once again. It fell on my head
and cried thrice: 'Croak, croak, croak'.

I was ecstatic, I would be a king. Almost
immediately, I had another heart attack.

The post-mortem report revealed:
I had died even before the third croak.

Sudeep Sen
(India, USA and UK)

THE NISHI'S CALL

Its call is the sound of hot molasses syrup,
of ripest mango and candyfloss tenderness.
It stalks the streets and passes below your window;
it stops outside your door and moans its wild distress.

It can sound like your loving mother, passed away,
or your dead father who once held you to his chest;
it can sound like your own sweet sister, brother, friend,
or your darling child, your nearest and your dearest.

Beware! The Nishi walks the night with piercing cry.
It's the most haunting creature you can imagine.
Don't answer the Nishi's call. It's a soul-snatcher
and your voice is a silver cord it will reel in.

The Nishi carries an empty earthen vessel
to trap your soul if you answer its tempting cry.
When morning comes the Nishi's dead will rise again,
so close your mouth and ears or you will surely die.

A creature of night and of nightmares, the Nishi
stalks the streets and holds vigil below your window.
Its call is the sound of candyfloss tenderness.
Do not answer for it will snatch your soul and go.

Debjani Chatterjee (India and UK)

The Nishi: a part of Bengal's folklore. A creature of the night, it
gathers the souls of the unwary, deceiving them by calling in a
familiar voice.

SARASWATI'S BLESSING

My brother Raj and me eagerly
Wait for Saraswati Puja:
She would bless our schoolbooks.
We make chains of coloured papers –
Red, blue and green.
Dad bought them from
Calcutta's New Market.
We stand on stools,
And hang them high
Criss-crossing to form a roof.
Dad and Uncle Ravi lift
The Goddess up and place her
Under our decoration.
I gaze at Saraswati seated
On her pedestal. She fixes me
With her painted wide eyes.
Her red lips, slightly parted,
Move as if for a second.
I hear a voice, and then it's gone.
Soon we are told to go to bed.
In the dark, Raj whispers
'Which books did you leave
Under her feet? I like her blessings
On my Maths.' 'English. She told me,
I'm going to England one day.'

Asit Maitra (India and UK)

Saraswati Puja: Hindu festival in honour of the Goddess of
Learning and the Arts.

THAT ELUSIVE BIRD

Poems of Inspiration

CRADLE-SONG

From groves of spice,
O'er fields of rice,
Athwart the lotus-stream,
I bring for you,
Aglint with dew
A little lovely dream.

Sweet, shut your eyes,
The wild fire-fiies
Dance through the fairy neem;
From the poppy-bole
For you I stole
A little lovely dream.

Dear eyes, goodnight,
In golden light
The stars around you gleam;
On you I press
With soft caress
A little lovely dream.

Sarojini Naidu
(India)

Neem: the Margosa tree. It has many medicinal and other uses.

STRANGER

No moon, no stars in the deep dense dark,
what mysterious reflection wakes in me?
I am a stranger, waiting for my eyes to open,
absorbed and anxious, I have counted lonely hours
alone in my mother's womb – my own waiting room –
waiting for a zodiac sign to tell me my life's moves.

As the sunflower lifts its head for the sun to shine
so my heart longs to see my mother's face.
Flooded by the earth's radiant light
I will see my mother – a vision of beauty!
A growing cord of joy draws me into this world.
Within myself, I light the lamp of arrival.

Rashida Islam
(Bangladesh and UK)
Translated by Debjani Chatterjee

This poem is in the voice of an unborn child in its mother's womb.

IF ONLY I WERE

The chameleon wind blowing over
    the rugged ranges of the Himalayas.

A tree in full regalia of autumn
    on a peacock-blue lake in Vermont.

A bee upon a raft of sunlight
    in the gardens of this nurturing earth.

A coral formation along the Great Barrier Reef.
    The robe of the night sky filigreed with stars.

A jugalbandi raga at dawn
    of sitar and shehnai, sarangi and tabla.

A wild flower greeting the weary
    explorer in some forgotten desert.

A rainbow poised over the Iguacu Falls
    chanting *make me always the same as I am now*.

If only I were Mother Teresa's eyes
    watching over a sick, sleeping child.

A dream come true in the warm smiles
    of all the children in our world.

The healing hands of a surgeon,
    the defence of innocent folk.

The biting, trusting grip of a new-
        born child at the mother's breast.

The voices of poets, thinkers, artists, the words
        of inspiration in the struggle of our daily lives.

Shanta Acharya
(India and UK)

Chameleon: tropical lizard that can change colour.
Great Barrier Reef: the largest coral reef in the world, in the
Coral Sea off the coast of Australia.
Filigree: delicate ornamental work made from gold, silver or
other fine twisted wire.
Jugalbandi raga: an Indian melody.
Sitar, shehnai, sarangi and tabla: Indian musical instruments.
Iguacu Falls: spectacular falls in southern Brazil, two and a half
miles long and descending into the Iguacu River.
Mother Teresa: a saintly Catholic nun in Kolkata.

PARROTS OF LAHORE

(For Basir and Hassan)

These flashing, squawking whisps of green
hang round the schools, almost unseen,
and talk of where and how and when
they'll change the world and then again
how it might turn itself quite round;
they flit through air without a sound.

Composing lyrics from on high
they're just like angels in the sky
and though their songs contain great thoughts
the message is not heard in courts
or palaces of kings or lords;
their quills as fine as any swords.

But though their songs remain unheard
by all but other kinds of bird,
they give great pleasure and amuse,
when all seems lost they do not lose;
these parrots' words do travel far
and bring some joy in times of war.

Simon Fletcher
(UK)

185

AFTER LISTENING TO BEETHOVEN'S FIFTH

As if the ocean whirled
As if the air whispered

A mysterious laugh
Broke the depths of silence.
Light dripped from the face of night.

A deep sigh.

Was it midnight or break of day?

The sun turned its face.
The earth with trembling hand
Touched the hand of the sky.
Men, trees and birds embraced one another.

Mazhar Tirmazi
(Pakistan and UK)
Translated by Ajmer Rode

DAILY REMEDIES
(For children of all ages)

Daily wash face with wonder,
brush teeth with honey and oil of clove;
treat itchy eyes with dewdrops and rosewater.

Swab ears regularly with raga and symphony buds;
massage body with sunshine and olive oil,
then allow to run wild outdoors.

Gently rub kisses into cuts and bruises;
let long hours of sleep cure aching limbs.

Treat tantrums with masterly indirection.
Listen with sympathy, slowly divert attention
towards anything that distracts them from distraction.

Answer all questions with imagination,
feed their curiosity, stretch their creativity
with stories taller than the mightiest oaks –
reaching out for the sun, moon and stars.

Deal with stubbornness in much the same fashion,
with games, myths, songs, magic and pure illusion.

Shanta Acharya
(India and UK)

IN THE HAPPINESS OF ALL

My joy will be in the happiness of all,
   I will weep at everyone's sorrow,
I will distribute my own food
   to those who have none.
My flower-garden will provide
   flowers for everyone,
the clay lamp in my house
   will give everyone light.
In my house the flute will play
   the tune from everyone's home,
There will be no more gap between
my house and everyone else's.

Jasimuddin
(Bangladesh)
Translated by Debjani Chatterjee

Jasimuddin was a famous poet of twentieth-century Bangladesh.

I DON'T KNOW MUCH ABOUT INDIA

Some bits about the Raj,
subjugation under Clive,
old tales about colonials
and princes who'd all thrive
on wealth which they'd amass
from the masses they'd deprive,

and those Indian MPs we had
in eighteen ninety-five,
and Gandhi waiting patiently
for midnight to arrive,
and the tiger and the Gypsy
and their struggles to survive,

and the curries and the cups of tea
and cricket matches I've
enjoyed, and *The Jungle Book*
by Disney, and I jive
to 'Brimful of Asha
on the 45'.

Nick Toczek
(UK)

Raj: British rule in India.
The name 'Gypsy' comes from the mistaken belief that these
travellers were Egyptian. They were also dubbed 'Romany'
because they were believed to be Italian. In fact, they came from

India, having fled as refugees from eleventh-century wars.

Clive: Robert Clive (1725–74) was a British adventurer who worked for the East India Company and amassed a fortune in India.

1895: the year when Liberal MP Sir Dadabhai Naoroji (Britain's first Indian MP) lost his seat in the Westminster Parliament and Tory MP Sir Mancherjee Bhownagree was elected.

Gandhi waiting patiently for midnight: the Indian politician-saint Mahatma Gandhi is called 'the Father of the Nation'. India won independence from Britain at midnight on August 15, 1947.

The Jungle Book: a children's book by Rudyard Kipling, made into a popular movie.

'Brimful of Asha/on the 45': a song.

THAT ELUSIVE BIRD

It is a good-news bird,
dreamy, starry, with elfin eyes,
one day it will arrive here, one day,
in this city
from across the forest.

To watch that bird coming
people line the streets,
their eyes searching the sky
to see that bird come flutteringly.

That storm-beaten bird with its bright beak
will land on the road
and everyone will go after it.
That heavenly bird will bless the city
with good news.

But where is that elusive bird?
There is no sight of its wings yet.
The people go back indoors
every night to sleep and dream:
'One day that bird will come.'

Shamsur Rahman
(Bangladesh)
Translated by Tamara Hussain

Shamsur Rahman, born in 1929, is a renowned poet of
Bangladesh.

HAATH MILAO – LET'S SHAKE ON IT!

Hand in glove
  Through thick and thin,
Heart to heart
  We'll never part,
So *haath milao* –
  Let's shake on it!

Hand to mouth
  Our lives may be
But shoulder to shoulder
  We stand together.
So *haath milao* –
  Let's shake on it!

Hand in hand
  We share our lives,
Toe to toe
  We face our foe.
So *haath milao* –
  Let's shake on it!

Debjani Chatterjee
(India)

Haath milao: a Hindi and Urdu expression for 'shake hands'.

WHERE THE MIND IS WITHOUT FEAR

Where the mind is without fear and the head is held
    high;
  Where knowledge is free;
  Where the world has not been broken up into
    fragments by narrow domestic walls;
  Where words come out from the depth of truth;
  Where tireless striving stretches its arms towards
    perfection;
  Where the clear stream of reason has not lost its
    way into the dreary desert sand of dead habit;
  Where the mind is led forward by thee into ever-
    widening thought and action –
Into that heaven of freedom, my Father, let my
    country awake.

Rabindranath Tagore
(India)

ACKNOWLEDGEMENTS

The editor and publisher would like to thank the following for permission to use their poems in this collection:

Shanta Acharya for 'Faith', 'If Only I Were' and 'Daily Remedies'. Asif Ahmed for 'The Jungle'. Shafi Ahmed for 'Bedeh', published in *The Redbeck Anthology of British South Asian Poetry* ed. Debjani Chatterjee (Redbeck Press, 2000). Moniza Alvi for 'When Jaswinder Lets Loose Her Hair', 'Map of India' and 'Indian Cooking' published in *Moniza Alvi's Carrying My Wife* (Bloodaxe Books, 2000). Giles Andreae for 'Chimpanzee' published in *Come to the Carnival: Festival Poems* ed. John Foster (Oxford University Press). Anon. for 'Bengal' published in *The Children's Book of Comic Verse* ed. Christopher Logue (Piccolo, 1979), and 'I rolled them in turmeric . . .' published in *The Subhâsitararatnakosa*, compiled by Vidyâkara, ed. D. D. Kosambi and V. V. Gokhale (Harvard Oriental Series, vol. 42; Cambridge, Mass., 1957). Safuran Ara and Debjani Chatterjee for their translations of Mehrun Nessa's 'Gifts Of The Past Week' and Assiya Khatoon's 'The Fly'. Asian Young Women at AWAAZ Asian women's training centre for 'As An Asian Young Woman / I Am Expected To . . .' published in *Meri Zindagi: Poetry and Prose by Asian Women from the Awaaz Course* edited by Leonie Kapadia, Janet McDermott & Seni Seneviratne (Awaaz, Sheffield, 1998). David Bateman for 'Hot Spell'. Gita Bedi for ''Ere She Said' published in *Grass Roots in Verse* ed. Arif Ali & Catherine Hogben (Hansib Publishing, 1988). Mina Begum for 'From Sylhet To Sheffield' published in *Daughters of a Riverine Land* ed. Debjani Chatterjee & Ashoka Sen (BWSG Book Project, 2003). Buphinder Singh Binning & Debjani Chatterjee for 'Snakes Alive!' Rajat Kumar Biswas for 'A Lascar's Song' published in *The Lascar's Song* (1995). Debjani Chatterjee for 'Hungry Ghost' published in *A Little Bridge* (Pennine Pens); 'Little Old Man' published in *One For Blair* ed. Chris Searle (Young World Books); 'Pride Shot' and 'An Epic Abridged' published in

Animal Antics (Pennine Pens); 'Lakshmana's Regret' published in Albino Gecko (University of Salzburg Press); 'The Last Mountain' published in *Dinos, Dodos and Other Dead Things* ed. by Brian Moses (Macmillan, 2003); and 'A Fistful of Mud' published in *Saffron Tea* ed. Kampta Karran & George Tolis (Heaven Tree Press); 'Haath Milao: Let's Shake On It' written for the Barbican Centre in London in 2004; 'More Than I Wear' written for Calderdale Museums and Arts and 'Mehndi Time' written for Kirklees History Service; and for her translations of: Gulshan Ara's 'I Am A Daughter Of A Riverine Land' published in *Daughters of a Riverine Land* ed. Debjani Chatterjee & Ashoka Sen (BWSG Book Project, 2003), Safuran Ara's 'Abroad' published in Songs in Exile (Sheffield Libraries, 1999), Nasir Kazmi's 'The First Rain' published in *Generations of Ghazals* edited by Debjani Chatterjee (Redbeck Press, 2003), Yogeśvara's 'Look At The Cloud-cat . . .', Sunirmol Bosu's 'Grandpa's Nose', Rabindranath Tagore's 'Holiday'and Jasimuddin's 'In The Happiness Of All'. Debjani Chatterjee and Basir Sultan Kazmi for their translation of the latter's 'Among The Flowers' published in *Generations of Ghazals* edited by Debjani Chatterjee (Redbeck Press, 2003). Sukanta Chaudhuri for his translation of Sukumar Ray's 'The Owl's Love Song' published in *The Select Nonsense of Sukumar Ray* (Oxford University Press, India, 1987). Contributor to First Words for 'Grandmother' published in *First Words* (First Steps, 2001). Saleha Chowdhury for 'A Poem Of Joy'. David Cobb for 'Haiku' published in *The Iron Book of British Haiku* ed. David Cobb and Martin Lucas (Iron Press, 1998). Stanley Cook for 'Ramadan'. Ruth Dalton for 'Sonnemutu Speaking' and 'The Sound'. Brian D'Arcy for 'Oops! Don't Lose Your Head!' and 'Lords Of The Dance'. Ketaki Kushari Dyson for her translations of: Rabindranath Tagore's 'Big Sister' published in *I Won't Let You Go* by Rabindranath Tagore, trans. & edited by Ketaki Kushari Dyson (Bloodaxe Books, 1991), and her own 'Conversation Between Aunt And Niece'. Jeanne Ellin for 'My First English Curry' and 'But I Speak English Already'. Ian Emberson for 'The Snake-Charmer's Wife'. Nissim Ezekiel for 'Goodbye Party For Miss Pushpa T. S.' published in *Nissim*

Ezekiel's Collected Poems: 1952–1988 (Oxford University Press, Delhi; 1989). Simon Fletcher for 'Three Blind Men Describe An Elephant', 'Jewels' and 'Parrots Of Lahore'. Victoria Field for 'Full Moon, Lahore'. Bashabi Fraser for 'Tartan And Turban' published in *Bashabi Fraser's Tartan and Turban* (Luath Press, 2004), 'A Card For Me Mom' published in *Rainbow World: Poems from Many Cultures* (Hodder, 2003), 'Come Play With Me – It's Holi!', 'A Skipping Game' and 'The Song Of Hero Hippo'. Zulfikar Ghose for 'In The Desert' and 'The Remove' published in *Penguin Modern Poets 25* by Gavin Ewart, Zulfikar Ghose, B. S. Johnson (Penguin Books, London, 1975), and 'The Picnic In Jammu' published in *Jets From Orange* (Macmillan London, 1967). Chrissie Gittins for 'The Noodle Eater' published in Chrissie Gittins' *Now You See Me, Now You . . .* (Rabbit Hole publications, 2002). Prabhu Guptara for 'An Alien, I . . .' Amiti Grech for 'Boat Ride' published in bittersweet: *Contemporary Black Women's Poetry* ed. Karen McCarthy (Women's Press, 1998). Sue Hardy-Dawson for 'A Question Of A Snake' and 'Extremely Elegant Elephants'. David Hart for 'A Bus Ride In Birmingham'. Kaiser Haq for 'A Tropical Sunset'. Shakuntala Hawoldar for 'Language For Sale' published in *Multicultural Voices* (Mauritian Writers' Association, September 2003). Savitri Hensman for 'English Literature – GCE' published in *The Republic of Letters: Working Class Writing and Local Publishing*, ed. by Dave Morley and Ken Worpole, (London: Comedia Publishing Group, 1982). Tamara Hussain for her translation of Shamsur Rahman's 'That Elusive Bird' published in *Breathing Other Air* ed. by David Hart (Birmingham City Council Education Services, 2002). Rashida Islam for 'Mon-Doria' published in *Daughters of a Riverine Land* (BWSG Book Project, 2003). Anwara Jahan for her translation of Rabindranath Tagore's 'Bengali Language' published in *Free My Mind: An Anthology of Black and Asian Poetry* edited by Judith Elkin & Carlton Duncan (Puffin, 1992). Mahmud Jamal for 'Migrants' published in *The Redbeck Anthology of British South Asian Poetry* (Redbeck Press, 2000). Mike Jenkins for 'Nice Advice' published in Mike Jenkins's *Poems for Underage Thinkers* (Pont Books, 2004). Rudyard Kipling for 'The Ballad Of East

And West' [Extract] from *Rudyard Kipling's Verses 1889-1896*. Shamshad Khan for 'High Time' (published in *The Fire People: A Collection of Contemporary Black British Poets* ed. Lemn Sissay, Payback Press, 1998), 'Palm Print' and 'A Little Bit Different' – A Little Bit the Same'. Sitara Khan for 'Joys Of Ramzan'. Usha Kishore for 'Tanka' published in *'In the Ship's Wake'* edited by Brian Tasker (Iron Press, 2001), and 'Special Gifts' and 'Tiger'. Arun Kolatkar for 'A Scratch' published on the internet. Tony Langham for 'Eid Song' published in *Come to the Carnival and other poems* compiled by John Foster (Oxford University Press, 2000). Tariq Latif for 'A Harvest Of Wheat' published in *Tariq Latif's The Minister's Garden*, (Arc Publications, 1996). Asit Maitra for 'The New Gavaskar' and 'Saraswati's Blessing'. Nasima Masood for 'Dupatta' published in *Meri Zindagi: Poetry and Prose by Asian Women from the Awaaz Course* ed. by Leonie Kapadia, Janet McDermott & Seni Seneviratne (Awaaz, Sheffield, 1998). Thomas McColl for 'Muslim Girl At The Bus Stop' published in *In the Company of Poets* ed. John Rety (Hearing Eye, 2003). Irfan Merchant for 'Schoolyard' and 'Koh-I-Noor'. Spike Milligan for 'Hello Mr Python', published in Spike Milligan's *A Children's Treasury of Milligan* (Virgin). Brian Moses for 'The SSSSnake Hotel' published in his *Barking Back at Dogs* (Macmillan, 2000). Mustansir Mir for his translation of Muhammad Iqbal's 'To A Fearless Heart' from Tulip in the Desert: A Selection of the Poetry of Muhammad Iqbal trans & edited by Mustansir Mir (Hurst & Company, London, 2000). Sarojini Naidu for 'Palanquin Bearers', 'Coromandal Fishers' and 'Cradle Song' published in Sarojini Naidu's *The Golden Threshold*. Bibhu Padi for 'Pigeons' published in Bibhu Padi's *Lines From A Legend* (Peepal Tree Books, 1993). Uma Parameswaran for 'Amma, I Like School' published in *The Northern Durbar* ed. Brian Lewis & Shripathi Upadhyaya (Pontefract Press, 1997). Yogesh Patel for 'Typical Mr Patel's Typical Promotion' published in *The Redbeck Anthology of British South Asian Poetry* (Redbeck Press, 2000). Kailash Puri for 'Strength' published in Flame (Crocus Books, 1991). William Radice for his translation of Rabindranath Tagore's 'Palm-Tree' published in *Selected Poems by Rabindranath Tagore* (Penguin Books, 1985). Taufiq Rafat for 'Monsoon' and 'The Mango Tree' published in *Taufiq Rafat's A Selection* (Oxford University Press, 1997). Padmaja Rao for 'The Bird Feeder' published in *Poems of Cultural Diversity* (Kala Sangam, 1999). Lila Ray for her translation of Jibananda Das's 'Cat' published on the internet. Ajmer Rode for his translation of Mazhar Tirmazi's 'After Listening To Beethoven's Fifth' published in *Modern Poetry in Translation No. 17*. Selina Rodrigues for 'Leaving The Village' and 'The Picnic'. Kendric Ross for 'Flavours Of Asia'. Win Saha for 'Locomotion'. Beheroze F. Shroff for 'Bridge And Tea Party' published in *A Piece Of Me: Expressions Of Life By Asian Young Women* (Yorkshire Women Theatre & Yorkshire Art Circus, 2000). John Siddique for 'Helping Out'. Seni Seneviratne for 'People Ask'. Hamid Shami for 'Lost' and 'Mother Tongue' published in *Wish I Was Here* (Pocketbooks, Edinburgh), 'My talented cousin', and 'For Starters'. Shehnaz Somjee for 'The Street Healer Of Karachi'. Jon Stallworthy for 'Sindhi Woman' published in *Rounding the Horn: Collected Poems* (Carcanet Press, 1998). C. M. Lee Summerfield for 'Floods'. Pireeni Sundaralingam for 'Sri Lankan Schoolroom' published in *The Progressive*. Rabindranath Tagore for his 'Where The Mind Is Without Fear' published in his *Gitanjali*, and his translation of his 'The Further Bank' published in Rabindranath Tagore's *The Crescent Moon*. Nick Toczek for 'I Don't Know Much About India'. Geetha Upadhyaya for 'The Durbar In The North' extract published in *The Northern Durbar* ed. Brian Lewis & Shripathi Upadhyaya (Pontefract Press, Pontefract; 1997). Shripati Upadhyaya for 'Unseated' published in *Poems of Cultural Diversity* (Kala Sangam, 1999). Ravi Vangadam for 'Under The Alligator's Skin' published on the Indolink website. N. C. Wickramasinghe for 'Butterflies' published in *The Mighty Ark* ed. John Foster (Oxford University Press). Ian Wilson for 'How To Treat An Elephant'.